LIN

1

10

20.

THE SURPRISE OF BURNING

Also by Michael Doane

The Legends of Jesse Dark

THE SURPRISE OF BURNING

Michael Doane

JONATHAN CAPE
THIRTY-TWO BEDFORD SQUARE LONDON

First published in Great Britain 1989

Jonathan Cape Ltd, 32 Bedford Square, London WC1B 3EL

A CIP catalogue record for this book
is available from the British Library

ISBN 0-224-02599-6

Printed in Great Britain by
Mackays of Chatham PLC, Chatham, Kent

For Bradley,
for Christopher,
for Raymond,
and for Claudine

CONTENTS

THE SURPRISE OF BURNING

ORIGINS OF THE ARCHIVES

LONDON

1944

Feeling the tremor for the third time, she rises from the bed, certain that it is no mistake, neither nerves nor indigestion but a contraction; down low, an ache, growing sharp and then receding. Flow and ebb. Pulling her nightdress tight around her, she moves to the window and looks out across the dark street, counting the seconds to herself as though to measure the intervals. Five, six. Black and white, she is thinking. London at night reminds her of a photograph of a photograph in which nothing moves except the inky smoke rising from manifold chimneys: coal smoke, burning leaves, vapors of chemicals, the lacy ash of letters and newspapers lifted high from hearths and polluting the night. The inevitable colors of iron and of steel, of furnaces filled with rubber, old clothing, discarded dolls, fifty-one, fifty-two, a perfume of petrol, a silver steam rising from the streets, a white mist of her own breath on the window before her, and those unwashed cars parked like monuments out front, those cars that no one ever seems to drive away.

One thirty. One thirty-one. Only the middle of September and all of summer has gone up in that smoke, a summer that only calendars told of, that passed unnoticed while she'd slept and read and daydreamed within these walls, sometimes going to the cellar at night, when beckoned by the sirens. Alone with Daphne or any of the other women on the ward, the unwed mothers of Saint Jude's: Alice, Madeleine, Luisa, Judith, Anneka . . . some of the names made up, fashioned for these last anonymous months, something secret to go by. I call myself Ariel to hide my voice. When I sing it is to myself that I am singing.

One ninety-five. Only yesterday, after staying away for nearly a month, Daphne's man had arrived. Hat in hand and a forsaken bunch of violets to offer, saying he'd tried to hail a taxi but none could be found. The war, what. And he'd shrugged to ward off the purgatory of Daphne's gaze. Ariel had excused herself to leave them alone, had wandered the hallway for a lonesome half-hour, her hand down low as if to hold the child there. She had dilated early, weeks ago, and had been told to stay in bed whenever possible. If the water breaks, when the water breaks. The high tide of birth. And the baby seemed to know; he seldom moved, never kicked, but lay in repose within her fragile space, hearing, perhaps, those same sirens they all could hear.

When Daphne's man had departed, Ariel had gone back to the room to find her sitting up in bed, calmly tearing up the violets and dropping them one by one to the linoleum. "Better," she'd said, "that there be no father. That this baby bear my name and not his." She'd tossed the crumpled violets toward the window, missing it by three feet. "That's what I told him. Better that this baby bear *my* name, I said. And I have said as much to the administrator."

Two forty. Two forty-one.

She'd expected boredom, tedium, vast spaces of longing and discomfort; life without a man being only a half-life. Instead, she had been placid, alert, even cheerful, tending to a garden of coverlets, pillows, cotton nightgowns, her swollen breasts and belly, the daytime radio sounds coming in through the open window, those English voices hailing and halloing, and the music of Daphne's daily weeping in her private corner, those wet sobs of he'll never come, he doesn't care a twig about me, not even so much as a simple letter . . . and on, on. Dirigibles hang gray as cheap pearls in the distance while arc lights define and redefine the scaffolds of cloud formations. There is a whistling from down below and a droning overhead. Three twelve, three thirteen. Down the street is an impoverished gunnery station, the turret almost always at rest, four barrels pointing skyward toward an absent enemy. No one has yet shot down a flying bomb, three twenty, three twenty-one.

There it is, dull, coming on, yes, another. Three twenty-one was the count: five and a half minutes. Has she counted too slowly? Too quickly? Start again, to be certain. Five, six, seven . . .

She allows herself for once to think of the past, the recent past, inventories of Saint Jude's and the strict regimen of bed-changing, linen, windows open no matter the weather at 9:00 a.m., and all the pregnant women marching the hallways, up and down the stairs, working those legs, getting the blood moving, breathing in, out, and the endless plates of boiled vegetables steamed of all color, everything finally resembling potatoes, even the once-green beans and, one eleven, one twelve, the warm milk they served in tin cups, the aftertaste of metal, and, no, a twinge but not a contraction, ah, and hardened pastries offered by some neighborhood group, the whole East End now a hotbed of civic action, even insofar as unwed mothers in wartime, poor dears, we'll bake them stones, that's what we'll do. Daphne, receiving a letter from her mum, had cut and folded it into a tiny white carnation and hung it over her right ear, saying, "Tell me this is pretty, you. Tell me you're green with envy."

"Burning."

"You don't look it. You're too cool, too happy. Like you're glad to be having this baby."

"I am."

"Even if 'e won't have a father?"

"There are many fathers. So many I can't count them anymore."

A pause, a reflection. "You're wicked, is what you are."

There, another. Five minutes, this time she is certain. Count again;

no need to hurry. The night is growing longer and deeper. It is not even midnight yet. Count. How many seconds have already passed? Ten, twelve.

She starts at fifteen and counts too quickly up to thirty. Backtracks to twenty and arrives at fifty-one when she feels it again, too sudden, and so much sharper this time. "Daphne?"

But the girl is fast asleep, her face turned to the wall. At the foot of her bed a night light burns a dull glow. A Madonna, of all things, a tiny glass mother with a package of baby in her arms, lighting a patch of green linoleum next to the door.

The pain comes in a spiral, the turning of a key, then subsides. She can no longer count. Turning away from the window, she heads for the Madonna, beyond the Madonna, the door. At Saint Jude's there are no doctors or midwives. She'll have to go up the road, they've told her, to the hospital, to have the baby. Everything is prepared, everything is waiting for her there. Twelve, sixteen, twenty, she counts despite herself, and steps into the hallway, where the night nurse sits hunched over a magazine. "I think," she says aloud, but not loud enough to be heard, "I think the time has come."

The hall is painted yellow and white; yellow up to four feet and white across the top. The wall is lined with portraits of the apostles, reproductions of works by Protestant masters. She never knew that Saint Peter had worn a ruffled shirt and waistcoat, all of England is full of such news, thirty-six, thirty-seven, she arrives at the night desk and plants her palms along the edge, saying now, it's time, please have them come for me. The nurse lifts her head and smiles, answering, "Yes, pet. Right away."

There is no wheelchair or comforting shoulder to lean on. She'd expected something else somehow. The nurse hustles down the hall to a telephone, cranks out a number, and repeats the address three times, spelling out the name of the clinic, J as in Jesus, U as in utopia, D as in divine . . . "Right this way, dear." She feels a heavy hand on her forearm, steadying her. One lone hand of a stranger and nothing more. They are descending the front steps when she feels her water break, the warmth rushing down her thighs to her bare feet. The night nurse doesn't notice. She is watching the sky, where the arc lights have been turned on, their beams waving like arms across a sea of cloud. "What will it be tonight?" she muses. "Rain or bombs?"

Springing for another pint, Slope downs a mouthful and then turns, takes the three darts offered him, and steps to the line. He plants his left toe *just so*, juts forward his jaw, and cradles the first of the darts between round thumb and callused forefinger; winking once, he aims. The point is not to squeeze too hard, to simply *let* fly, leaving the elbow and shoulder out of the picture, using only the wrist, searching for an almost flat trajectory. Twenty, twenty, six. The last dart having slipped. Cursing, Slope steps aside, leaving his place to his mate.

His game is off a bit but no matter, he is having a grand time, by now halfway blitzed and ready to make a night of it after having been on call for three bloody days and nights, riding the wagon from fire to fire to pick up various pieces of humanity. With flying bombs and whatnot wreaking havoc round the East End, the ambulance brigade is doing overtime, like in '41 and '42, only now, his hands not so quick at the wheel, old Slope is no longer a driver but a back-seat attendant, a porter, a stretcherbearer. Roger's got the wheel now, the wanker, and that makes *him* the boss, though the day he starts giving out orders to the Slope is the coldest day in Hades. Roger and all his pimples, his stuttering, and his way with women. Watching his mate rack up a sixty, Slope downs his pint and orders another. "On the slate, darling. Slope is here to stay."

Roger sits at a corner table chatting up a dolly and drinking from a pint of something evil-looking, one of those black-brown beers from up north, bitches' brew. Says it turns them on, the ladies, gets them all soft and lazy and obliging, but later on, if they get a call to a fire, there'll be Roger pissing against a pile of rubble his bladderful of the useless potion. Wanker. Slope considers that he couldn't have pulled a worse partner from under a rock off the far coast of Lowestoft. Whenever the war is over, if it ever is over, Slope'll see the back of him once and for bloody all.

"You're up, Slope."

Stepping to the line, he balances the flechette in his palm, curls it upward into the sling of thumb and forefinger, and lets fly. Twenty, six, twenty. Still ahead of the game but not by much.

Colin Slope, just turned fifty, is a lifelong bachelor, still up for a bit of nip and tuck himself, which, bless the war, is a damn sight easier to find these days, all this *mortality* going around, making what was once a fair waste of a man a sudden prize in the arms of many. Just last week, in the chaos after a strike, he'd come upon a trembling young thing huddled in a doorway. A skinny slip of a girl, no more'n seventeen, scared half out of her wits and asking him over and over again, did he see it, did he *see* it? He'd seen it, whatever it had been, flying bomb or delirium tremens, and when he'd fluffed up her skirt and started working on her underthings, she'd gone limp on him, holding her arms loosely around his neck while he'd unbuttoned his fly and gave her a hump or two. Mortality, Slope considers, is a fine thing after all, a hard and fast reminder to him to take her where she lays, having world and time enough to lay them all, if only they'll remember their ever-blessèd mortality, the only thing that'll ever make them give their precious selves to Slope. Slope, the half-cripple with a face that broke his own mother's heart. One day it's a scared rabbit hiding in a doorway, the next a homely missus boo-hooing into a kerchief all the lonesomeness of hubby gone off to Normandy; today the back streets and tomorrow the front parlor. It's more than four years now that Englishmen are dying like flies, and that leaves only more on the table for Slope; more hunger, want, need, these countless female vacancies left untended in the wake of duty and death. Slope merely obliges, forgoing the tip of his cap, the finger-kissing, the pouring of Chablis, the proffering of blood-red roses. He takes her where she lays, in the here and now, and in his arms, her back pressed up against the cold brick, she fairly stinks of it, that mortality, that promise of *not surviving*.

The dart round finished and Slope again the winner, he buys a trip to the bar for himself and his mate, what's-'is-name, and when the telephone rings he freezes for an instant, certain it's for him, but no, it's some lad calling for Libby, nothing to fret over. Anybody heard any bombs out there? It's quiet as a convent, it is. Heinie's maybe taking a day off for a change, his chamber spent, needing time to reload.

"Another go, Sloper?"

"I won't say no, mate."

Twenty, twelve, six. His mark veers leftward, the tilt of alcoholic gravity doing its damnedest. He'll remember that his next toss and compensate a hairsbreadth or two. That's the trick, knowing where you limp and where your blind spot lies. Walking over or looking past. One leg withered and the other strong enough for two. One glass eye and the other eagle-sharp. Slope survives; he compensates.

"A pint of bitter, love."

Then, without thinking, he is standing in the back alley, fly undone, pissing against a blank wall, lifting a scuffed shoe away from the stream. My God, I'm pissing *uphill.* There is no one in the alley but Slope and an audience of stars that grow long and thin when he gazes upward through the smoke and the low clouds. Whatever is in the war, he is catching it; the heaviness, an unbearable weight. Even in firelight, he sees only the edges of the flame. More and more his vision comes from what he cannot see, the shape of darkness defining what is there. To see what is in front of him, he has to turn his head, the askance is so much clearer to him than the straight-on. Overhead, there are two moons, one emerging from the other, both of them the color of warm milk, while those stars burn hot and cold. It is a lovely night for the war, and all in all he regrets not having had a fire to attend to. He misses the wailing and the cursing that go on, the sirens and the unraveling of water hoses, the pulling down of long-useless walls, the progressive undoing of the bedeviled East End, while the women clasp their own bosoms in the fire shadows, anxious and yet relieved, their juju bags of hair, fingernails, holy cards, and bits of love letter having saved them from ultimate darkness. They stand and titter in the periphery, or they weep, or they simply stare, and one of them, always one of them at the very least, is merely waiting to be fucked. Slope packs it back into his fly, buttons up, and heads grinning back into the pub, taking a dart in one hand and a pint in the other. Slope aims, releases, and the dart nestles into the red heart of the round black eye, a winner.

He doesn't hear the ringing, he is too deep in his drink, and it is Roger who must rouse him. "It's us, Slope. We're on call. Move it, old man. Right this way."

Holy God. The war again. Insatiable, she is.

He drains the last pint, blows a red, wet kiss to Libby, who only shrugs, and heads out to the wagon, a converted lorry. Out of habit, he takes the driver's seat and is bumped over by Roger. Grabbing a Player's, he can't find a light, but the boy has got a match in front of him, the glow almost blinding, and Slope turns his head just a mite to get a fix on it, lighting up.

"Bomb strike, is it?" he asks the boy.

"No such luck. A maternity run."

"You're bloody joking!"

"Valentine Place. You know the way?"

"With my bleedin eyes closed."

"The good one or the glass one?"

"Just you drive, boy. Just you drive."

Rain she don't fall, wind she don't blow. Words for a jazz song but no one's singing. Just past midnight and the street is as empty as a church. The nurse, shivering, removes her arm from around the waiting mother and folds her arms together, hiding her hands. The mother bends, feeling another contraction, stronger this time, and more frightening. A warmish water, her own, trickles down her leg. "Do you know the time?"

"Five past twelve. Shouldn't you be sitting down? Standing will cost you all your water."

The mother sits on the step and contemplates her hands. One day has become another as the contractions have increased in frequency. Every few minutes now.

"Boy or girl?" the nurse wants to know.

"What?"

"Which do you prefer, a boy or a girl?"

"Oh, I don't . . ." *Hurt. Again.* There, there. Down low. Catching her breath. "I don't know."

"I've two girls at the house, fourteen and ten. No trouble at all, those girls. Never be soldiers at least. Not in this war."

A bouncing boy; a giggling girl. She's thought too little of the afterward of tiny hands, feet, bobbing head, spitting, crying in the night, wet linen, pins, creams, glass bottles in boiling water. She hasn't even considered any names beyond *son* or *daughter*.

"Just so you're keeping the child," the nurse tells her. "Father or no, a mother should stay with her baby."

The snarl of an engine startles them as a motorbike rounds the corner at Blackfriars Road and sputters off down Surrey Row.

The nurse wants to know if she knows any lullabies.

"Wha?"

"Something to sing to your child."

She says she knows a few. "The blues, mostly. 'From Here to Tuesday.' "

"Can't say I know that one. Sing whatever you can. Children need their songs. Especially at night, when they can't sleep. When the dark . . ." She turns left just as the lorry, siren wailing, rumbles through the intersection of Webber and Valentine and heads for the front step.

Swinging open the cab door, Slope descends on shaky legs, signaling for Roger to leave it in gear, he can handle this one alone. Two figures emerge from the shadow of the doorway. The expectant mother wears a long white nightdress and is barefoot. "Good heavens," the nurse says. "I never even thought . . ." Opening up the back of the lorry, Slope lowers the steps and leads the woman upward into the back, where a cot is set up on either side, the legs fastened to the lorry wall. The woman sits and he reaches downward for her feet, lifting her legs so she can recline; then he turns to help the nurse, who only waves him away. "You're not coming?"

"I'm the *night* nurse," meaning to say she is alone and cannot leave the other mothers to themselves. What did he expect? "There's a war . . ."

He says he knows. There's a war on. What other excuse to leave a bleedin blind man with a crippled leg to take care of a pregnant woman in the middle of the bleedin night?

"Do you know where you're to take her?" the nurse asks.

"To the Royal," Slope tells her.

"Which Royal?" she shouts.

But Slope isn't listening any longer. Turning toward the woman, he tells her to lie still. "We'll be there in no time." Thinking to himself that the pub, doors closed and windows covered, will stay open till two. World and time enough for Slope.

"The Royal Eye," says the nurse to the closed doors.

Slope swings open the latch window leading to the front of the lorry. "The Royal Waterloo," he says. "You know the way?"

Roger nods and kicks the lorry back into gear, pulling away from the clinic. Taking no chances on his mate's sense of direction, Slope guides him through the open door, telling him to turn round at first chance and head straight up Waterloo Road. "And none a your fancy left turns this time. We got a mother with us." He slams the door and bolts it, sits on the cot next to the mother, and takes a good long look at her. Decent legs, slim, and breasts looking heavy enough for a pair of hands, but of course that belly distorts everything, maybe it's really a bird without that baby, though her face isn't too bad either. She looks scared, is what; fright in a woman always has an erotic effect on Slope and this one's fairly brimming with it. The light in the lorry is blue and in the shadows her face is contorted with pain. Reaching a hand across the distance, he touches her shoulder, telling her to go easy, they've only a short ride, ten minutes at most. She begins to breathe differently, taking great deep gasps, sucking at the air and then blowing it out. He asks her if she wants to take his hand and in answer she reaches and grasps. Her hand, small and blue, fits into his like a round stone, and he can feel a throbbing there, like the beating of her heart making its way up her arm and into his palm.

Roger swerves the lorry left and right again and Slope curses him through the wall. "Shell hole!" is the explanation. London's full of them, these blooms of empty space across her eastern patch. Can't gather up the debris fast enough, and these mounds of rubble rising like thick tree trunks from the street are no match for Roger, who drives like a waiter cruising among crowded tables, denting a bumper here and there, jouncing over shell holes and rubble alike, muttering to himself about getting there, getting there. A full about-turn at Blackfriars Road, backtracking up Ulford Street, a quick right to The Cut, slanting left toward Waterloo Road. No fun in simplicity; fancy's what takes the cake. Roger dances the lorry round Lambeth SE1, getting there, getting there.

Her fingers tighten round Slope's and she says a word or two but he can barely hear her through the noise of grinding gears. "He's coming," she says again. "The baby's coming."

Too soon or too late. Slope drops to his knees and lays a prayerful hand to her belly, saying no, not just yet. Five minutes, ten at worst. *Later.*

"Help me," she says. "He's coming. I can feel it."

It isn't a voice he's heard before, except maybe at the pictures. Holding his free hand against her stomach as if to stay the birth, he tells her to hold on. World and time enough, he says. There's world and time enough, dolly bird. But then she's crying out, something about dear God or whatever, and he at last places the accent. "You're a Yank?" he says. This war a never-ending chain of surprise and guessing and tosses of the dart.

She whispers that she's American.

"Then you can bloody well wait till we get to the hospital."

But she can't. Lifting herself upward from the cot, she raises her knees high and Slope, incredulous, sees her pull back the nightdress and there she is, starkers, and already the head is emerging, blue and frightful, as the lorry swerves once again, Roger calling "Shell hole!" in apologia. The woman is crying aloud now, thrashing her head back and forth on the cot, letting go of his hand and then reaching for it again, the head now coming into view, bringing with it a wash of afterbirth, waters in blue and a black blood. She is pushing and screaming but there is no more movement, the baby seems to be caught within her, and Slope, letting go of her hand, reaches between her legs, not knowing what to touch, what to reach for, and Roger swerves again, too wide this time, and the lorry swings to the left, tossing Slope upward until he is nearly on top of the mother, his face next to her open mouth. She is screaming one long note to him and then the lorry tips over onto its side just as Slope can hear the explosion drowning out the scream and all other sounds in the London night.

He awakens on the street, a small fire burning close to his outstretched hand. Straight above, sick stars wink at him through waving wands of smoke. Reaching his hands upward, he caresses the length of his body, inventorying for blood, broken bones, torn muscles. Nothing, not even a bruise, as though angels have laid him on that exact spot, a pillow of harmless stone beneath his spinning head.

Rolling to his side, he sees the overturned lorry just ahead, the back doors opened wide and inside only the haze of smoke still lit by the blue lamp. He struggles to his feet and feels a lightness in his face, something missing, and realizes that he has lost his glass eye. Focusing with the good one, he sees fires burning all around him, the buildings to either side filled with flame, and, taking his first step, he nearly treads upon—what's this—a baby wailing in the middle of the street. Can't be. Is. A splash of blood like an inkstain across his tummy, fists raised high, shrieking to Slope to *pick him up*. The old man bends and takes the child in his arms, then limps over to the lorry, where he sees clearly enough the dead body of the mother through the smoke, and farther on young Roger, head poked through the windshield, neck half severed by the broken glass. No one else is around. Slope is alone with the baby and the burning. To his right a flaming brownstone and to his left the ruin of a pub, its windows shattered and signboard askew: The Glass Eye, something of a namesake. Slope knows the place, *knew* it; had been well oiled there now and again during the worst days of '41. He'd like to cross himself but his arms are full of child. Where's the bleeding Red Cross? All he can see is fire and now here's someone with a camera taking his bloody picture, and him without his eye, shameless. Picking his way through the rubble, he arrives at the end of the street, beyond the burning, a few steps from Waterloo Station. Up ahead, a church is aflame, its stained glass lit up with an inner life, the apostles seeming to jitterbug, the Holy Spirit in the form of a dove shaking its flaming tail. Waterloo Road is already crisscrossed with firehoses and the sky is filled with spray. Slope heads north, toward the Royal Waterloo Hospital, but when he arrives at the corner of Waterloo Road and Tenison Way there is a woman wearing a cape and cap taking him by the arm, leading him out of the ruin and across the road. She is reaching to take the baby from him, but he resists, holding it tight in his arms, thinking to himself that it must be another of those hysterical mothers, child lost in some fire or another, come to the scene of the tragedy to find her child again. "Who in hell are you?" he wants to know and she flashes her Red Cross badge before his eyes, same badge as his, and although he still isn't willing to hand over the baby he follows her up Tenison Way, hoping when they question him that no one'll notice the beer and whisky on his breath, he could lose his job, and when they arrive at Belvedere Road Outpost and at last he surrenders the baby to a nurse's waiting arms, they sure enough hand him first of all a form to fill out, an incident report no less, asking name, date, place of incident, and all he can remember is the Yank lady, Roger Masters with his neck cut in half, and The Glass Eye burned half to the ground. So that's what he writes, careful not to sign his crooked "Slope" at the bottom, and when he's certain no one's watching, no eyes of the war that might later call him a liar, he drops the form on the registrar's desk and limps out of there, back toward the lorry, to see if he can't find his missing eye.

IN WHICH PAGE, TAKING RANDOM PICTURES, HEARS A SIREN

NEW YORK

AUGUST 1974

This much I know. The rest is only rumor. I was born during a V-strike, in London, in 1944. The explosion tore me from my mother's womb, killing her and leaving me blind for the first three years of my life. My father was and is unknown. I was given to the Red Cross and there the doctors examined me for wounds. Cornea, pupil, iris, and retina: all were intact, as were the optic nerves. I had a normal brain and lively reflexes. Though I seldom blinked, my pupils opened to the stimulus of light and closed when it went away. Figure this: I simply *refused* to see. Perhaps I was gazing elsewhere than upon the planet that had so brutally acknowledged my coming. Perhaps I was mourning my mother. The images and lights and shadows, passing through the naked lens, left no imprint for me to recognize. I was written into the file as a traumatic since there wasn't much else to be written.

What I remember of that dark infancy: Lying in cool water while warm hands bathed me, lifted and clothed me, and laid me in a chair to rest. Traffic in the street and a wood floor and the sounds of footsteps on that floor, a perpetual coming and going, the wind of women walking past me. A man smelling of dust coming daily to scratch a cross on my forehead and then touch my closed lids with salt water. I am told that I seldom cried, that I was a quiet child, and not unhappy. But that, too, may be only rumor, the witnesses unreliable.

There was a war on and the V-strike had destroyed the hospital and all of its records. I was found on the street, wailing to be picked up, near a burning lorry with my mother inside. My guardian, a diplomat named Page who later passed his name on to me, sifted through the ruin of London to find out who my mother had been, and the truth was a nasty surprise for everyone. She'd been a singer of jazz and blues, nearly a legend, who'd disappeared many months before, and by the time they knew that the body in the burning lorry was *her*, the war was already ended and she was only another casualty, famously dead. I was two years old by the time they'd identified her. That's when the search for my father began. Her divorced husband denied me. He hadn't seen her in years, he said, and no blood tests were taken. Only hearsay was left to go on. Perhaps the husband was lying and had reconciled with her for a single night somewhere between New York and her London hideaway. Or it might have been her saxophone player, J. Skate, who is said to have loved her and searched for her when she'd vanished. She sang men like songs. That much is written. There was talk, but no evidence, of a lover of many years, an anarchist named Valentine who'd spent time in prison. A composer, a recording engineer, a fan, a stranger. The leftovers of rumor and namelessness. Blind alleys that I have come to know by heart and doorways leading to empty rooms. I've read her biographies and each of them has a different ending, mystery and requiem in place of fact. She was a siren and she went up in smoke, a fitting end to the legend of Lela Maar. Even her name bears the patina of rumor. She made it up, like so much else, inventing a self she could love. And for all I know she invented me as well, fashioning a son without a father, something only a legend could do. What matters the seed when the womb is where I come from? His hand pulling her close to him and his breath upon her face: making me and then dissolving like a burned film.

Figure this: to see, it is not enough merely to open your eyes. The gesture in itself is only the beginning, as in a theater the opening of curtains *precedes* the spectacle. Eyelids, curtains, the shutter over the lens. This much I know and the rest is only rumor: to see, you must open more than your eyes; the rest must follow, the heart, the soul, and the unforgiving shock of memory. Memory, not history. I search the memory of my father, his echo in me, in the history and souvenir and archive of my mother.

I was taken in by Armand Page, an American diplomat whose wife never loved me. I was *his* keepsake from the war and the missus kept her distance. I lived with the Pages until I was fifteen, when they died together in a flaming Ford. I'm warning you. All of my parents go up in smoke.

We lived, through the end of the war, in London, where I was cared for by nannies and that man who daily blessed my eyes. I saw nothing but the dark sky above my bed, a blueness, indigo, incoming waves. Later, when my stepmother moved back to New York, I lived with Armand in Paris and was cared for by a Frenchwoman who read me stories in her own language. She was the first vision of my lifetime. Her face. Even then I knew better than to call her Mother, though I remember wanting to many times. When I was four years old, I moved to New York with Armand, my sight restored, a 20/20 vision that has proved to be a mixed blessing. I grew up to become a photographer, specializing in war. That's the short of it. The long of it, like any lifetime, is not so simply put.

A lifetime witnessed in the rear-view mirror. Going somewhere and seeing where you've been. I've lived in shitholes, mostly. War zones and the like in Algiers, the Middle East, a number of patches in Southeast Asia. Vietnam, the green place, the hothouse, home. Now I'm back and standing in the middle of the street, hearing a siren different from the sirens I know by heart. Dee-dull dee-dull in Paris, whoop whoop whoop in Berlin, and a haunting eee-EEE in Jerusalem. I've just gotten off the bus, most of a fifth of Jack Daniel's still roiling my blood, and someone is screaming at me from the sidewalk. The Manhattan sky, framed in glass, filters grainy sunlight through gray clouds. The siren has a name, ƎƆИA⅃UꓭMA, and a private voice is telling me to hit the deck, heavy incoming on the way, so I step aside at the last possible moment and the ambulance flashes past me, three tons of steel on the way to a disaster. For once, I am too weary to follow.

No one asks me if I'm all right, although a bum, eyeing my leaky knapsack, heads up the concrete in my direction. He watches as I reach into my bag. "Hey, lissen . . ." His hand reaches toward me just as I flip the lens cover and push the shutter. My camera aims through a hole in the knapsack at 1.4 frames per second. Shickashickashicka. Too bad there's no film, I could send these shots to some art-world magazine, photos of thirsting humanity in black & white are always good for a few hundred.

"Lissen," the man tells me. "Lissen, I'm aching for it. You god a boddle in that bag. That one, am I right? Something?"

I tell him I'm looking for someone.

The bum shakes his head. "I don't know nobody."

Whir click whir click. I'm still shooting blanks.

"Do I have to know somebody? Is that it?"

I dig deeper and fondle the bottle. I'd been drinking from it on the bus from JFK to Grand Central and before that from LAX to JFK. All that's left is two fingers of what had been a ten-finger bottle; the label came away hours ago under my fidgeting fingers. The bum takes it with both hands, grasping, forgetting of course to say thanks, saying only that he still don't know *any*body. "Who *should* I know?"

But already I'm climbing Fifth Avenue like a stairway, 43rd, 44th, 45th. Crossing west at 45th Street against the light, I feel my knee locking up again and so hobble to the curb, swearing. It's the right knee, the cursed one, and I bang it with my knapsack, hearing a ping or two, metal against metal somewhere in the exchange, but the Fiberglas cap won't give and I have to yank it into place with both hands.

The army surgeon had told me to avoid long walks. Pavement is the worst, though stairways are entirely taboo. "Overdo it and later you'll be able to unscrew your calf like the lid on a Mason jar." The doctor's advice: "Standing on your head for fifteen minutes or so a day will relieve the phlebitis. Sleep with your legs elevated. Stay out of drafts."

"What else?"

"Sign this."

"What is it?"

"Your eviction notice. You're going stateside, one way."

"I've already been there."

"This time you'll stay there."

I was wounded going back for the boy. No, that isn't true. I went back for the boy, found him, signed for him, and shipped him homeward. I should have taken the same flight but contact wasn't finished for me. One last run up the pass, I told myself. A last hand at the poker game and then I'd fold my cards and split. Losers always play *one more hand*.

I shouldn't even have been in the game, having already quit the scene four months before. I was cooling out in New York, getting used to beds and paved streets, neon lights, and the deadly silences of no contact whatsoever, when I heard Dune Buggy was dead. A lot of people were dead, theirs and ours, but Dune Buggy had been a friend. We lived together during my second tour, him a soldier and me a photographer in 1972–73, in a house outside Saigon, to the south, where the heat was bearable and the incoming was far away. Chulin was our housekeeper at first, then she was Dune Buggy's wife, even if the army wouldn't recognize it. I loved her, too, but Dune Buggy loved her more. She kept house, did our laundry, cooked our meals, and washed our shot glasses. At night she kept Dune Buggy company, and in Vietnam that was what passed for love. He didn't have to pay her anymore, she was his for free. Big American guy with a crazy smile. She was taken with that smile more than anything else about him. He never stopped smiling, even in the bush when the heat was on.

The house was full of my pictures, the worst of them, unpublishable stuff. Dune Buggy pinned them up wherever there was available wall space, keeping the war right there for us, close by and unforgettable. A head on a stick. A severed hand clutching a stone. A baby in four pieces like a rag doll. In the outhouse was a contact sheet of a pile of burning corpses, the flame moving from frame to frame according to shifts of wind, pictures taken during the monsoon, when someone decided to burn all these bodies in the rain. Those photos were the connection between contact and R & R. Like a dotted line, without a signature. We lived with Chulin for almost two years, alternating between forays into the north and west and lazy weeks of sitting on the back porch, watching our garden grow. There was a bamboo platform overlooking the garden and we would sit drinking beer and Jack Daniel's and listening to American music of any kind to drown out the droning of insects. Now and then we'd shoot up beer bottles and litter the garden, until Chulin asked us to knock it off, we were too drunk and she only loved us sober. The garden was wild and overgrown, the ground covered with broken glass and dead palm fronds, rotted mangoes, and the corpses of birds.

There was a kind of berry growing in the brush, I never knew the name of it, that the birds would come to feed from. In early summer the berries were green and poisonous and the birds would die in swarms. Chulin would go out with a rake and a basket and gather up the corpses like fallen leaves. Later, when Dune Buggy and I weren't around, she would burn them in a pit and cover them over. In the late summer those same berries turned black, and after feeding off them the birds would perch high in a nearby tree. One night, while Dune Buggy and I were getting loose on the back porch, we saw these birds falling one by one from the tree. There were dozens of them flapping around in the weeds, but it turned out they were only drunk instead of poisoned, and in a few hours they'd slept it off and flown away. The next night they were back and again the tree was raining birds. They came every night until that tree was stripped of its fruit and then we never saw them again.

When Chulin was pregnant, Dune Buggy said he'd marry her, and of course the army refused permission. There were several kinds of marriage in Vietnam but only an army marriage was binding enough to ensure Chulin a way out of the country. We were told the sad story of a Marine who'd married a Vietnamese at the town hall. When he'd finished his tour he hadn't been allowed to take her back with him. No papers. And when he'd refused to leave without her they'd thrown him into LBJ, Long Binh Jail, to rot until he came to his senses. Since Chulin was half Chinese, even the Vietnamese wouldn't marry her to an American. So we scouted around for a Catholic mission and found a French priest who agreed to marry them with French papers in exchange for a hefty dose of morphine. We hadn't seen any clinic and mentioned the fact, and the priest said the clinic wasn't there anymore. "The morphine is for me," he said. "When prayer fails me, it helps me to sleep."

So Dune Buggy was married to Chulin by a junkie French priest who gave them *colonial* French papers, about as worthless as Confederate money, and the baby was born five months later, during the rainy season, while Dune Buggy was up north, leaving me alone with mother and child. He was baptized Catholic, Dune Buggy's choice, and given my first name, which I never go by: Hunter. When Hunter was only a few months old, Dune Buggy came back from a month of LRP, long-range patrol, with a whisker of shrapnel in the forearm. He'd had worse wounds, but this was the first since he'd become a father, and he insisted that I become godfather to Hunter.

"This is serious business, Page. Don't take it lightly."

I didn't, but he wanted me to sign something anyway. "I trust you," he told me. "I just want it written down."

So we wrote up a letter like a mutual promise, him writing what he wanted of me and me writing that I agreed, then we signed it twice each, dated it, and got a friend of Dune Buggy's to sign as witness.

"Godfather means you watch out for his ass, Page. If I buy the farm. Take care of Chulin, too, if you have to. You know what I'm saying?"

But the center wasn't holding and our gravity was breaking up like cheap coal. In the field, the line between malice and mischief was growing razor-thin. I found myself increasingly uninterested in the spectacle of war and I was seeing less and less contact, taking pictures of sunsets, trees, Chulin, and Hunter, instead of tanks and obliterated babies. I was independent, neither AP nor UPI, and I didn't *have* to go out there anymore, except out of a lifetime's habit of following war in a kind of hypnotic stupor. This wasn't my first war. I'd grown used to the jungle, the weird green of it, and the drugs, and all the rock and roll that went with the place, but now I was broke, not selling any pictures, and the contact almost bored me. I was very tired, and living with this *family* began to do me in.

Here is the note I left Dune Buggy and Chulin:

> Holding my breath now. I've come and gone often enough and I won't be back. Teach Hunter English and get him the hell out of here. One less Page. I'm going home to fill in the blanks.

Dune Buggy had three more months in and then he planned on slipping westward, to Thailand and on to France. Those bogus papers wouldn't get his family very far, but Chulin spoke French and they were counting on luck more than anything. He'd of course be going the route of a deserter. You're never out of it till you're back in the States, and Dune Buggy wouldn't have time to get that stamp on his release form.

I had it easier. Hitching a ride on a transport plane, I hung around Hawaii for a few weeks of decompression, then took a commercial flight to the mainland. There was a letter waiting for me in San Diego, from Dune Buggy. Chulin was dead. With all the ways to die in Vietnam, from bullets, mortars, mines, bamboo spikes, grenades, fire, blades, and poison, the heat, the rain, the insects, Chulin had died as though in any faceless suburb, crossing the street and getting hit by a car. One of those little French cars, I imagined, a rusted Peugeot without fenders, the kind of car we often saw on Saigon streets. Dune Buggy wrote that he'd sent Hunter to the French priest. "I know he's a druggie, but who isn't around here? At least he's reliable and it's only for three more months." Then he'd moved north with his division. The letter didn't say where he was headed.

Dune Buggy never used the words the others used. *Wasted* meaning dead. *Deleted. Canceled.* He always said *bought the farm*, a phrase I usually associated with old men. Others *cashed their paycheck* or, in AP terms, *fell in the field*. After I'd been in New York for a month, still looking for work and trying to publish a collection of my photographs, I got a letter from the priest, written in French. When Jane read it to me, she didn't translate *mort au combat* with *bought the farm*. Dead in combat. Come for the baby.

Dune Buggy had a mother in Ohio who was unimpressed that the baby had been baptized. He'd never even written that he was married and a father. If what I said was true, why hadn't he written it? "And even if I believed you, what do you want me to do?"

So I went back. I had a piece of paper that said I was a godfather and what I was to do if David Ambrose, Dune Buggy on his helmet, ever died. I had a French-colonial marriage license and a birth certificate handwritten by the Saigon doctor who'd brought Hunter into the world. Before leaving, I asked Jane to marry me. That would make it legal, the adoption, but she said, Wait, hold the phone. "I have reasons for marrying you, Page, but this isn't one of them." So I went back cold, without a plan, waiting for a guardian angel to show his face. The whole country was strewn with babies, thousands of them the fruit of passing soldiers, no surprise to anyone, and it turned out that now that Dune Buggy was dead, Hunter's passage to America was a snap. It was Chulin they didn't want, or any of the Chulins, but Hunter, slanty eyes and all, was by this time an American or, as a lieutenant in archives told me, *one of ours*.

As such, he was welcome in the U.S.A. and I had only to wait around a few weeks for the paperwork, vaccinations, and a grilling from an assigned chaplain asking why in hell I was doing this anyway.

I said I'd known the boy's father. "He's got my first name."

"So he does. And what does that prove? He'd be better off here, among his own."

"How's that?"

"Back home, he'll be a freak. An American, sure, but still a yellow kid from somewhere else. An alien."

I didn't have the words. I never have the words. All I could say was, "When he's older, I'll be there to answer his questions."

"What questions?"

"About his father and mother."

The chaplain was annoyed. "Hell of a note," he said. "Be there to answer his questions. Suffering Christ."

I should have gone with him. There was a transport plane filled with medical personnel, a brace of nurses from a children's hospital, and I put him on it, alone, leaving him with a woman on her way to New Jersey. "Jane Sanders, West 85th Street, Manhattan. The address and phone number are written here. He's my namesake, take good care of him."

"Any message?"

"For whom?"

"Jane."

"Tell her I'm on the next plane."

But I wasn't on the next plane, nor the one after that. I should have gone with the kid but I had that old-time feeling. The card game that should have ended at sunup but is still going on well past noon. One more time, lay it on me.

I was that hot for a last run up the pass.

I limped around the White Rose for a few days. It was a bar where strung-out journalists swapped stories and stayed loose, sweating through the dead periods between leads and picture-taking. When the pay phone rang and they asked for Page, we had to ask which one, me or Tim Page, an Englishman who had fought the same lens wars as myself. If I answered to my first name, there'd be a lot less confusion. I spent three days drinking whisky and watching the fan's slow rotation, and then I got a telex from Jane saying the baby was in her arms. I took the first truck heading south, caught a chopper into the Zone, and descended, just for the hell of it, into God's green glen.

No one should stay there for so long. It's inhuman, corrupt. The earthly garden the farthest from Eden. The circle that never occurred to Dante, an en*joy*able hell.

And they wanted to see me gone, even after all the good times I'd shown them in black & white. "Time's up, Wide Eyes. We just signed you the armistice. Go back to the world and marry that girl. Do you remember her name?"

"Jane."

They wanted me to go worse than I wanted to stay. I'd grown too weird for them, too humanly like Nam for them to go easy on me. No one really believed that I'd come back for the boy, for Hunter. I'd come back for my own purposes, and it was time to cut me loose.

One last run up the pass, to contact, heat, and I spent a knee like small change and earned a medal in my forehead, a plate where once had been bone. Does it shine in the moonlight? I'd asked Nurse Nurse. *What?* Does it shine in the moonlight? I mean, does it shimmer or anything? Like a tiger eye? *I can see my reflection*, Nurse Nurse told me. *I'm not so pretty tonight, am I?*

But the skin graft covered it over, and now, in mirrors, I can detect only a gray shading to my forehead, in the center a black dot, reddish around the edges, like some kind of Hindu makeup.

You're damn lucky, Wide Eyes. You nearly got a frontal lobotomy for free.

I asked if it shined in the sunlight, in the moonlight, with a flashlight; when I touch it it feels cold, my lobella. Up the pass and into the bush, that's all I meant. Where the air gets so heavy you have to swallow it before breathing it and your chest is all bound up with rope, I mean fear, fear of being alive just barely. I used to be able to feel the blood all through me, even in my toes, you know, *throbbing* in my big toe with this kind of precision. I'd get a push from a white cross or two, enough to make the night last all night, that was my R & R, smoking a stick in a squat position while watching the stars burn and the tracers, three to the ten, raining from them. Once this Marine on acid got into a long ramble with me about tracers, saying they were star tears, the stars were spitting and weeping great gobs of heavenly flame all over us, the star gods were in a rage, and on and on. He had recently gone indigenous, stripping naked and smearing himself with swamp rot, nattering about the Path, the Order, the serpent swallowing its tail, and he'd written *Son of Death* on his helmet, a self-baptism so many of the grunts had undergone, naming themselves after what they'd become. Dune Buggy, High Priest, Ghost Runner, Coming Home, The Lone Stranger, Blackheart, Wide Eyes. We always went to sleep stoned and awoke on a ground grown harder during the night. And I always remember Son of Death standing up tall and straight, naked as any animal, in the middle of this savannalike glade *in the heat of battle*, fearing no evil, and reaching out his arms as if to catch the tracers. No chance of that, they were miles off, raining down on some distant bush where there might or might not have been NVA; the choppers weren't coming in too low like they didn't want to see if they were hit or miss, just putting on a show for all of us down there, high as hell, wiping away sweat and drool with the backs of our hands. On moonless nights we always loved to watch those tracers from our friends in the heavens.

"Can you hear me, young man? Are you all right? You've had a nasty fall."

What I need to know is, does it shine in darkness, in the black of night? Does it glow, does it glimmer? All I see in the mirror is a blue-gray shading covered with a wrinkly scar, skin taken from the soft inside of my thigh, a lump of flesh latticed in soluble gauze, covering a finely crafted metal brain pan.

Sirens, sirens.

"I think he's coming to."

I realize, a word at a time, that I've blacked out again, this time one of the more sudden, a pulling of the cord. I never have any warning, these things come on just like that, the sudden closing of the shutter, wink, and it's lights out. Other times I just fade, like someone's turned down the volume on the world and there's suddenly no sound track, the man in front of me is moving his lips, everything gets all overlaid with a cheap kind of film, and the pictures flicker before me so, so, slow, ly. The blackouts are more violent but less frightening. Black and white, black and white. One minute I'm cruising Broadway and the next minute I'm on the cement looking up at a circle of faces. A man in a three-piece suit bends to ask if I'd like a doctor.

"Nmm."

"Whaddy say?"

"Shut the fuck up, I can't hear him."

The first time it happened I was still in the hospital, Saint-François d'Assise, in Saigon. I'd gotten out of bed and begun to make my way to the latrine, hand over hand from bedpost to bedpost, my knee still filled with water and all kinds of evil that had to be drained off every few days. I'd struggled past my mates and was only two beds away from the crapper when I'd gone suddenly into the black and had awakened centuries later with my head cradled between Nurse Nurse's heavy thighs. "There now."

"Here. Now."

She'd been holding out on me for weeks, wouldn't even tell me her name, which was how she'd become Nurse Nurse, a woman lieutenant in this man's army, and now here I was with my skull cradled in her longed-for lap. *When I thought of Jane, I saw blankness, an empty picture frame. What I felt when I touched my own face. Gone.*

Was I imagining I felt her fur against my head, at least her heaving pelvic bone? Open your legs and hide me, woman. I've been wandering the jungle all these years for you. "If I said I was in love?"

She touched my wounds with her fingers swollen from the jungle heat. Knee, shoulder, forehead. "I would say we should get you back to your bed."

Then, once I was safely there, she moved her fingers from her lips to my own.

I awaken on Broadway to swarming flies and am helped to my feet by the man in the three-piece suit.

"You just fell," he tells me. "I've never seen anything like it. In mid-stride."

I assure him I am all right. "Just a little jazz in my blood. Nothing to sweat over."

"There's a Phoenix House just up the street here. I could take you there." He is referring to a halfway house, a methadone dispensary with a basketball court next door, very handy for midtown junkies.

"Not that kind of jazz," I tell him. "Personal jazz."

I wander through the debris of Times Square and go into a Nedick's, heading straight for the can. I rinse my face and dry myself with a grimy shroud that hangs next to the sink and then calmly watch the last beads of water evaporate along my forehead. At sixty-six frames per second, I can record the decaying orbit of my own skull. Shoulders erect, head back, eyes upon the stars and not the earth, or it may all come slithering out like a jarful of eels. If the hole had been any larger, they tell me, it would have been lights out. Or, a millimeter to the right, the shrapnel might have more severely damaged the premotor cortex and I would not have been able to make long-range plans. "The premotor cortex?" said Dr. Lipp. "The cerebral folds, curtains over curtains of foresight, planning, strategy. The great difference between you and me and a Neanderthal." If I am careful, if I mind my manners and my drugs, I've still got decades ahead of me.

The face before me in that men's-room mirror is a badly rendered mosaic. There is a scent of urine and despair and I find myself thinking I could have been a husband and father, or at least a more simple kind of nomad, instead of chasing all these wars and seeing life through a fish-eye lens with electronic zoom.

My anatomy seems to hum and chime when I move. In confined spaces, I can almost hear voices, languageless, Anglorussoswahili, and in the men's room, where there must be a high anechoic level, the hum becomes nearly a whine, almost a siren.

Page, get a grip on yourself. Easy, boy. Easy.

The reception grows progressively weaker, falling back into a gentle hum, a feeble vibration, and I can't help wondering if it isn't only my heartbeat, the emptying dry static of it, that I am hearing; the tick-tick of a heart, or of a clock, or of a bomb after all, after all, after all.

The only thing left to do is to call Jane. She answers on the third ring.

"Yes." As though in answer to a question.

"Jane. It's me, Page."

"Speak up, I can't hear you."

"It's Page."

"Listen, the baby's crying. Hold on a second."

I wait long seconds, the receiver pressed to my ear, having already blown the only line I'd memorized: *It's me.* From here on, I'll have to improvise.

"I'm back. Who is this?"

"Page."

She is holding her breath or searching for words. Then she says, "You aren't dead, then?"

"No. Still alive."

"Where are you?"

"In Manhattan. Not far."

"Are you coming?"

"Soon. Not tonight."

"Why not tonight?"

"It's too soon. I'm still in decompression."

"I don't understand."

"Just decompression." I'm uneasy blaming anything on these wounds.

Jane tells me she's lonely for me. "You're late again."

"Late for others is on time for me."

"I know. But I'd rather that weren't true."

"How's Hunter?"

"Adorable. Sleeping. Do you realize he's almost eleven months old?"

"I'm adopting him, Jane. You'll have to marry me."

"Page, that's blackmail."

"I love you."

"Convince me."

Not having the words, I hang up and call back two minutes later.

"You bastard, you woke the baby."

"Does he speak English?"

"I told you, he's only eleven months old. Give it time."

I tell her I will.

She wants to know where to reach me, where she can call, but I haven't decided yet between a hotel room and an empty doorway. Bedrooms are unsettling, ghost-ridden, silent.

"There's a message, Page."

"For me?"

"The police were here. Not really police. Army something. I thought at first it was for Hunter but they didn't even know about him. They're looking for you. Something about a picture you took. I'm supposed to call them if I hear from you."

"Don't."

"You didn't have to say that. What will you do?"

"Nothing. Decompress."

"You make it sound like a ritual."

"It is and it isn't. It's sordid and tiring."

"When you're tired enough, come lie down with me."

I tell her I will.

"And when you come, come to stay."

"I've been thinking about it."

"Now that you're wounded."

I admit it. Hospital nights of adding it all up and following the dotted line back to where I was loved.

I tell her I'm healed but not as pretty.

"You were never pretty."

"No. I never was."

What Jane first loved in me was the caged animal, cage and animal being, to her, inseparable. She was a kid, a student, four years ago, and I was back in New York for a lecture, moneymaking, and a shot at drying out that sponge in my heart. Since I didn't fit in anywhere, I was pacing a lot, unable to sit down, and she took that as evidence of obsession and pain. Our first time in bed she used her nails on my back, thinking I'd like that, but when I slapped her she understood at once that I wasn't the man she'd taken me for.

"That's a slut move. Insincere."

"I meant to please you."

"Please yourself first and I'll come along for the ride."

Scratching and slapping ended right there. So did the illusions. We spent two months together without saying a word about love and then I went back to the war for more pictures. When, in her first letter to me, she said she loved me, I took her for a moron, assuming one of us at least to have been intoxicated beyond reason. Then I decided it was the distance, twelve thousand miles of safety between the two of us allowing her to say what she felt and no harm done. Another letter came with a similar message, so I wrote back: "Stop being literary. We only fucked."

"Like hell we did. And anyway, love isn't literary."

To prove her otherwise, I wrote a letter in pencil, breaking down a bit. "It was love but I'm not there anymore. I'm here."

She answered that I wouldn't be here forever. "All wars end."

I answered that this one just might not. I might have been praying.

She graduated from Columbia and took a job in a gallery on Madison Avenue, doing catalogs mostly. I went back to visit in the fall of 1972, older and more full of drugs than before.

"You look like hell."

"I feel right as rain."

This time I didn't wonder about love. I was back, wasn't I? Though I worried that saying the words was a sham, an attempt on my part to join some tribal circle from which I'd forever felt excluded. An orphan's reflex. I felt blessed to fall asleep with her at night and then waken in the dark, put clothes over the ghost of me, and vanish. My instinct was to pay for her, as if to make all things equal, and I could never forget that my ugliness was no gift. I hadn't killed anyone but I'd seen more than enough of the dying, and the images of a decade had left overlaid stains, tap my chest, *here*.

"I'm going back, Jane."

"No surprise."

"It isn't finished yet. There's more to it than pushing the button."

She hated my photography and said she was unable to reconcile the artist with the art. I had put together a collection for publication and she had tried to censor me before the book could get to press. "I don't want this," she'd said when my book came out. "I wouldn't want these on my walls or on my bookshelf. Others show the glamour of war, or the sorrow, or just the dirt of it. Why can't you take a picture that doesn't look like a bad dream?"

Filthy habits last forever; there's no getting over them. The first picture I ever took professionally was of a woman bleeding to death in an Algiers square. The second was of a bodyless head. I hoped I could solve that black box of memory.

"Send me letters," she said, "but no postcards."

I promised nothing.

Once I was back there, the memory of her enraged me. She was my insanity. She had nothing to do with the rest of it. The slave in me had refused to take her picture and if I ever forgot her face, even for an instant unable to conjure it, I was deeply troubled. I had never noticed time before and now my hands were heavy with it. Night and day, day and night, nothing more. At night I could hear Dune Buggy and Chulin in the next room and I would grow angry with them. When they slept, I could not. For the first time I found myself suffering life rather than pissing it away mindlessly on danger. I felt mortal and I wanted to go home. Contact took on a new and not entirely unpleasant edge: if I died now there was someone to mourn over me.

Neon burns the August air, an odorless gas lighting the colored glass tubing like tribal torches along Broadway. The only sounds I hear of myself are the slight squeak and slosh of shoulder and knee and the Leica case slapping my hip with each uneven step. My thoughts drift from a man and a woman, Page and Jane, to men and women, to men, to a man, call him Father. As I said, I never found him. I found versions of him, any one of which might have been real or bogus, take your pick. At the moment, on the shiny street, I don't feel like *playing* Daddy for any child—or for Jane, for that matter. Still a caged animal, I'm thinking of my own sweat and blood and in the glare of Times Square I am stopped short by a rangy black hooker, haloed in light, her coffee breasts dripping with blue sequins, hotpants thrust forward, the zipper sharpened to a point. "Hah bah-tit?"

"How about what?" She is too tall for me, I've grown used to Orientals, small-boned and dainty, with breasts the size of my palms. This Amazon would take me apart, rewire me somehow, leaving my shoulder where the knee should be, the knee hanging below the armpit, and the wind whistling through the hole in my forehead while I breathe my last in some alley beyond Ninth Avenue. The night is still young and my thoughts are banging pinball-fashion from cushion to cushion—get laid or lay down with love?—and since I can't decide I do nothing but walk, going through another trauma over a hotel room or an abandoned doorway, where to sleep.

After Vietnam, America seems like an enormous Holiday Inn, with plush carpets and deep beds, sure, but too much pastel, too many towels, and conditioned air that is somehow frightening. In L.A., I'd taken a motel room and sat up until nearly four in the morning, punch-drunk from travel and unable to so much as close my lids. Going for a walk, I found a parking lot on the edge of the airport and laid myself down between two parked vans. I was asleep before my head touched asphalt, you explain it.

Pigeons dive and shit in random patterns and I find myself watching the ground for loose change. Heading downtown, I'm thinking of those fathers again, when I haven't thought much of them in years, ever since I gave up the search. Dr. Lipp had warned me: "The future may mean less to you," he said, "while the past may take on new meaning." The parameters have shifted, as the good doctor said, leaving a sense of lopsidedness, a distraction toward the past. On a sheet of paper he had drawn the "normal" graph,◁— • —▷, an equilibrium between considerations of past and future, stabilizing and identifying the present. "Imagine that you've been fitted with a superpowerful rear-view mirror, one with a refined telescopic lens. The future thwarted, the past thrown into clarity, thus . . ."◁═ • – – ▷"The doors of anticipation, if not entirely closed, are now only vaguely ajar for you to peer through. As one of the side effects, you may experience a heightened sense of mortality."

I decide upon a doorway. Beds can wait, and when finally I crawl into one it will not be alone. The Manhattan darkness is again as gray as a cathode ray, electrified and uneasy. Footsteps—spike heels?—click staccato on the pavement and someone is banging on a metal door, wanting entry. Still moving downtown, I find myself below the grid, where Manhattan loses its Cartesian logic, no more numbered matrix of Street and Avenue, these streets having been laid out by drunken Dutchmen centuries ago, nostalgic for the canals of Amsterdam, everybody wanting a place by the river and those living inland losing all sense of order and direction. I have always preferred the surprise of disorder, the accident of an alley or a cul-de-sac; the sign *No Exit* always makes my heart skip a beat. I am aware that I am still on a matrix of some kind, no matter how oblique or aslant, but in the night there is no way of knowing east from west or north from south, and x never leads to z by way of y.

In front of a record shop I stop for a moment to rest my knee, idly checking out the window. I don't know the names of anyone anymore. Since Jimi Hendrix I can't hear anything else. I am about to walk on when an album cover catches my eye, a face I've seen before: my mother. I've seen enough of her pictures to know well what she looked like and I recognize the cover photo as being from around 1938, that's how her hair was then, lifted upward and pushed behind her like a regret. On other album covers she looks faded, wasted by time, especially on those vinyl 78's, but this photograph seems as though it had been taken a day ago, my mother breezing in and out of the studio—"Like this, boys"—and landing here in a window for her son to gaze upon.

She was really something, Lela Maar. I wouldn't have wanted to know her as a child, but once a man, anytime. No one sang like her back then and nowadays a lot of people try but not many get there. Or I am only an admiring son, on bent knee, waiting to be blessed and forgiven for surviving her. She is a legend now and I will never know how much her dying had to do with what she's become to history. I was there but I am hardly a reliable witness. Ask the jacket cover of this album: "She sings. This is all we know of her in the end." I know a little more but what I know is hard to put to words and music.

I buy the record. On the back cover she is wearing a flimsy black gown, like something the wind might just blow away, leaving her as naked as her voice. Eyes closed, as in nearly all the pictures of her. Photographers had it hard in those days. Their film was like shit and nothing really defines itself as living in those old photographs. It's archive work, *so we'll remember what she looked like.* I'm not complaining, just observing. I have a thousand versions of my mother in a footlocker at Jane's place. In most of them she's a singer, but in a few others I pretend to identify her as my mother, a different kind of mythology altogether.

There are ten numbers on the album, dating from 1934 to 1944, a recent compilation of all her best stuff, and the album title is "Lela Maar Sings Harry Lord." Taking the record to the back of the shop, I settle into a booth to listen. A man taps on the glass, saying something that I can't hear. He opens the door. "Don't you want the headphones?" he asks. "That way you can listen without distraction."

He hands me a pair of black headphones and I fit them over my wounded head, settle my ass into a chair, then lay the needle on side A, first number, to listen to Lela Maar singing Harry Lord.

LELA MAAR SINGS HARRY LORD

"A LONG FALL INTO SHALLOW WATERS"

(3:48)

1934

Now it is raining that blues rain, the incessant falling. Now Harry Lord has played all the piano he knows to play. Now there is no more coffee in his cup and his pack of cigarettes has long been empty, crumpled, tossed to the floor with a gesture normally reserved for music sheets with notes of undried ink. Now the wind comes wailing up the alley and the rain falls aslant, hammering the window in syncopation. Now Harry has his song, another something to remain unpublished and unknown, notes to carry in his pocket like loose change from nightclub to nightclub, jingle and jangle, something new for no one on earth to listen to.

Baby, I wrote you this lullaby.

Darling, I heard only the wind.

Lifting his head from the keyboard, heart still beating in 4/4, he rummages through the ashtray for the best butt he can find, coughs once, lights up, and fills the room with a smoke as blue as his music. The thing about being hungry is the way it makes you write, but even though he can walk his hunger all the way to 52nd Street they still don't have to let him play it.

Now the rain is ended and the gutters swell. Now Harry Lord is at the open window, taking deep breaths of Manhattan air, reciting to himself the last of his biography as he looks downward through five stories of free fall, seeing in his mind's eye his body already on the pavement, face down, a trickle of red running to meet the gutter. Rain falling and bits of trash blown by the wind. Nothing in the lyrics but lonesome vowels, a's and o's, sighs and croonings. Harry Lord, a failed musician, jazz, blues, tone poetry, all for nothing but his own four very private walls, writes his latest song and doesn't give it a name. A strange piece that he wouldn't call jazz, 2/4 here and 4/4 there with a heavy hand, dead slow, ♪= 60, just the kind of music Fingers long ago told him to forget about.

Three long dresses, hers, are hanging in the closet. She'd brought them in while he'd slept and hung them there, the red one, the white one, and the black one. First she'd listened to him while he'd played some of his stuff, then she had sung for him, then she had stripped the lonely tree of his body and laid her flesh upon his. *Compose me*, she might have been saying, but what he heard was wordless vibrato. When he'd come in her he'd felt a bolt of pain down low, a taking of more than he'd given. She had slid from under him to the other side of the bed, then reached a hand to his, saying "OK now," and he hadn't known what she'd meant. Later, she'd risen from the bed and pulled her dress over her head, smoothing it across her thighs. The rain had begun to fall, leaving the room as dark as closed eyes.

"I have to go," she'd said. "To get my things. My other dresses."

He'd answered that it was past midnight. Couldn't she go in the morning?

"In the morning I sleep. Stay where you are. Warm the bed."

He had lit a cigarette and watched the smoke form clouds above his hands. Then he had slept and had awakened to rain. Next to the bed he'd found a shoe box filled with cheap jewelry, earrings, bracelets, a black cigarette holder, a lighter shaped like a fish, the flame coming from its mouth. When he rose and opened the closet door, her three dresses were hanging there like listless dancers. She was wearing the blue one, had come and sung in it, taken it off, and tossed it to the floor while folding herself across the mattress, then had put it on again and left him half asleep in a warm bed.

Now the night is ending and the music has all been played. The nightclubs will be closing and half-drunk musicians will stumble Chinese-eyed from their caves to the dewy street. Now Harry Lord steps away from the window and sits again at his piano, still wondering when she'll be back and why she didn't stay, knowing that if he plays just now, at the dawn of the first day since Lela, if he plays he might awaken someone, upstairs or downstairs, East Side or West, in heaven or on earth, anyone.

You say you want the history but all you really want is superstition or legend, something to sell the record with. Whatever I tell you, truth or lie, you write it down and that's history but that don't mean it's the way it happened. Just you write it like I tell you and maybe it won't sound like journalism. You can throw in some chitchat about music and such if you like. Dotted eighths and tremolos and bridge chords and dissonant progressions. That kind a talk looks good in print, specially on the back of a album cover.

Lela Maar was a made-up name. She thought it up all by herself as a way of gettin out a her past skin. The word is *metamorphosis* but that might not fit right on no album cover. She was never entirely one thing or another, always slippin in and out a faces like makeup or old clothes. I'd guess she was never really naked like that, just plain Vera Marshall with goose bumps and lonesomeness. She was always a whore and a angel and a real fine singing voice and to Harry Lord she was both inspiration and ruin, they was always the same thing to him anyway. He wrote the music like he had to and she'd mess around with it and then sing it. She undid everything he made and made it better, and just because she had other men didn't mean he'd get back on her and go find himself other women. He never did. He just sat home and got old.

When they was living up on the West Side they never had no parties, never invited no one, no whites and no niggers, musician or civilian. Hattie used to go by to read the mail to Lord. He was dyslectic, you know the word? Write that down. I'm not making up a thing, you know, this ain't no jazz piece, just a interview, am I right? Hattie couldn't read much bettern me and I never got past the third grade, but Lord didn't mind her cause she had a speakin voice that did something good to him. Maybe it was just the sound he liked and not the words. Words was for Lela to fret over. She wrote almost all the lyrics.

You been by to see Skate? He's old as shit, like me, and I hear he can't get up his wind no more. Too damn bad. His sax went dry as a bone years back but I still got my fingers and an easy octave wingspread. Look at this right hand, these five blackbirds all in a row. A slow, Negro, arpeggio. Those are words to one a my own numbers, you never heard it cause it never got recorded. Lester Mink, he's a asterisk or a footnote, yeah, but I'm the one can tell you the history and not the bullroar, all that legend stuff makin gods out a simple hard-workin singers like Lela.

How'd you find me, anyway? They don't know me here. America sure has been home to me but I never once sat up front on the keyboards and had those lights shinin down on my music and my name. They know me in Paris, though, in those basements they still playin in, stayin up all night and just jammin. Least that's what I hear. A slow, Negro, arpeggio. I got a ticket for a boat ride and I'm plannin on going that way to find out if it's true. Is Lester "Fingers" Mink a star in Paris? Something to find out when you're eighty years old, who in hell you been all your life. Maybe I'll go places Lela went. Maybe run into her, who knows? I hear she's dead and she had this kid over there, but all I hear is that Lela lives, man, and it may not be just that legend stuff again. She change her name and hide out. You say you're somebody and who's to say otherwise? She never wanted to be whole, Lela. She wanted to be pieces a things, remnants, a lot of tied-up ends, so that when times were bad she could just unravel and turn into something else. Maybe that's the truth a what happened, that whole mystery a her leaving the country and where she went. While she was missing I read all kinds a theories in the papers and none a them come close. Like, she died of a overdose or she was murdered, stuff like that. I knew better and I never said a word till now. Isn't that her on the tape set? "Lela Maar Sings Harry Lord." Thirty years, long time. That song there, I never heard it till after she was gone. I took her to the boat myself and that's the gospel goddamn truth of it. She got on a boat and that's when she disappeared, far as this world was concerned. When I heard about this baby a hers I thought a lot about it and I don't know if she was carrying it when she left or not. If she was, she didn't say so. And no way was Harry the old man. She didn't go near him for weeks before she left, at least as far as I know. She had other men, maybe. Even when the drugs was getting her down and skinny and sad-looking. Lela Maar always had these men.

Anyway, then she was disappeared. That was the story at the time and now it's the history. Lela Maar is missing. Lela Maar just up and gone. And then we was hearin she was dead over there and all we could do was believe it.

All the same, you know, I don't believe in anything I read. Not even when I wrote it myself. All I know is, Lela Maar got on a boat with a suitcase and a trunk and maybe or maybe not a little baby hiding under her sweater. We took a taxi together from Times Square to the wharf and when I let her go she said, Fingers, take care, and I said you, too, Angel, and I didn't wait around to see that boat shove off but she was on it, that much I know. The rest is just talk as far as I'm concerned. All we can do is make up how it ended.

We all used to shy away from Harry, because he seemed too much in need a something we felt he'd never have. You hate to see that much want in anyone's eyes, even once, but Harry always had that look, worse than hunger, almost a panic, man, he walked into a room and either you heard the blues or some really screamy violin, I don't know which. He was moody and that moodiness carried over into his music, and even though *we* all knew that fame was a whore, Harry thought she was a lover, that was his style, elegance in poverty, man, he was desperater than Lady, too bad he didn't have the talent.

We called him Whispers cause a the way he used to sing. He was working in some pretty out-a-the-way nightclubs, half empty even around midnight, and maybe he had a nice touch on the keyboard but his voice had all that Lordy panic in it and he couldn't seem to get the notes off the tip a his tongue. *Get home*, I used to think to him, hearing him play like that. That wasn't a compliment in those days, not like *Bring it home* was, not the same thing at all. All I remember liking about his stuff, early on, was this little way he had of taking a beat down about half below the known bottom of the scale, this little ring-finger signature that made you touch ground just a bit, it was a nice touch even if he overdid it now and then.

I knew Lela before I knew Harry. She come to New York around 1930, 1931, and went straight to Fletcher Henderson for an audition that must a lasted all of four bars. She had a voice, yeah, but so do wild animals, and there was no way she was gonna get picked up by any name band in the city. Before meeting up with Harry, she made just about all the rounds, got herself a bit of work in a club down by the docks, and mostly she just scuffled by like about six thousand other singers, everybody in those days was fighting for work, like always, and anyway Lela was *too* virtuoso, and that's not easy for a jazz singer to be.

We were all in and out a work, in and out a love, in and out a the rain. There was this writer, Solomon something, who fell in love with Lela and Lela fell in with him, loveless. She was needing a place to sleep days and to hang her few dresses, a place to hide now and then from the jazz-hall creeps who took her for a whore just because she wore clingy dresses that showed a patch of tit or a triangle of thigh. No way to explain without singing it that it was the uniform of the business, jazz is always something sultry, and to be honest she sometimes did spend her late nights and early mornings *elsewhere* while Solomon the writer was out on the streets looking for her. His kind a love was a shepherd's love; he took care of her and seemed to love her more whenever she strayed.

Me and Lela got to be friends about this time. We was into smoking muggles, marijuana, just the two of us, cause the club we were playing in wasn't too cool, down near the East River, *low* down, and the Irish cats that used to come there drank bottoms up and had big fists and only barely tolerated skinny black me on the keyboards. Provided, of course,

I smiled and didn't tell them it was a Mary Jane, and not a coon, pearly grin I was wearin. Lela's singing took a turn about this time, though she still had a habit a taking off on these crazy vocal arpeggios and her phrasing was more often than not from the wrong side a the street. We'd roll our muggles into Lucky Strikes so the micks wouldn't much know the difference and we got into this thing with words between us, taking any word about giving or passing and making them all mean the same thing in sharp or flat. Light the radio. Pour me a cigarette. Turn on the bourbon, kiss the ivories, pass the trombone. It was our joke, and not even the sax player, a spade like me but *serious*, could understand us. Solomon neither, and he wrote poems.

He'd come to the club every night about midnight and just stand back by the bar, drinking pretty heavy in those days, all that time on his hands and Lela, too, and he'd just wait for her to get finished so he could walk her up the island to home. Lela said he had a rich family over in Brooklyn that sent him money once a month, thinking he was going to school, and he went home every weekend with textbooks just to make it look good. I asked if his poetry stuff was any good but she just rolled her eyes, meaning Hopeless, then she asked me to wrap up some muggles for her and I saw thirty-seven sundowns in her eyes.

I don't even know if Solomon liked our music. He didn't seem to have an ear for jazz. He was the type that'd listen to Bing Crosby, I guess. Something like that. Music with ribbons on it and teardrops made to order. I don't even know if he liked Lela's singing, though he was there so much he must a known every note by heart. One time, while she was singing up a hurricane, some clown at the bar started making jokes about her, cause she was sweating so much, getting *into* the song and it was a hot night; this guy was saying, someone told me later, that she looked about like she was in heat, a bitch in heat or some such thing, and maybe even he was sincere, but Solomon didn't get the point of it and he felt obliged to take the guy on. You know, *honor.* Solomon went behind the club with this guy and we found him after the gig, sitting in a pile a garbage, brushing eggshells off his jacket with the few fingers he still had that wasn't broken.

Nobody knew me in those days. Nobody knew any of us and you can't believe these stories of all the people who claim they come to see us at the wharf in those days. Me and Lela never played together again after that gig, we went our separate ways, it was like a fluke that we ever got together in the first place, she was so hot and me so cool, but just for a while she got me to playing it *her* way, like she did later with Harry Lord. Sometimes, when things at the wharf got too slow and the mick owner would close up early, we'd take the subway up to 52nd Street to listen to the gods. Mine was Lennie Tristano, who went blind from influenza and was for me the man who invented cool jazz, the lord of legato, who wouldn't dot no sixteenth note to save his life. Even if we hardly never had the bread to get inside, Lela knew all the doormen along 52nd Street and we even got in the Famous Door once or twice to see Count Basie and afterward Lela said, You'll be better than him, Fingers, one a these days you'll play that man six feet under, but I didn't see it that way, I always seen myself as just another nigger piano player. He played storms and I played rain, depends on where your heart is what you want to do with your fingers.

About five years ago I was in this club in San Francisco and there was this skinny white singer with long blond hair who did a whole number on Lela's stuff, starting out saying it was a honor to be here tonight, twenty-five years since she disappeared, then her voice kind a broke a bit before she got in singing "From Here to Tuesday" and she sang it real well, she had a voice for it, about the same pitch as Lela'd had, burning through the skin a your temples, and afterward I told her she was good, really good, and she'd go far, like I used to tell Lela without believing a word of it. I'd just say things like that to keep her going because she wanted it so damn bad. She was really corrupt, Lela Maar, and I mean that in a nice way, if you follow. She was corrupt with her music and all the shit that went along with it, and if she overdid everything, drinking and screwing around and never sleeping much, it was that corruption of simple naked need, like she couldn't sing enough so she couldn't live enough. Nowadays there's whole rafts a singers working on that number. You know, the tortured-artist effect. It looks real good under the lights and makes for a fine album cover. I'm not saying you gotta live it to sing it, just that Lela did, that's all.

Our gig at the wharf broke up when she met Harry Lord. About dawn one morning, she came to my place all in a mess. It was raining and she looked like hell, her hair all wet and her makeup every which way, like her face was a puzzle some drunk had put together. All I had was the bed and one chair, so I pushed all a my clothes off the chair and told her to sit down.

"I got a hot plate," I told her. "I can make you some tea. Warm you up."

"Right," she said. "Light me up some tea." She meant muggles. "Pour me a cloud, Fingers. I been walking all night."

I made the real tea first, heating up the water on my hot plate and pouring it into a coffee cup I stole from the club. Then I rolled up the marijuana in some newspaper cause that was all I had to roll it with and Lela smoked the whole thing herself.

"I met a man," she told me when she felt like talking. "He's got a song, a good song. I sang it all day and then I walked all night. You want to hear it?"

I said sure but then there was somebody knocking on the door.

"It's Solomon. He followed me here. He's been following me for two days. Don't answer."

But I can't not answer the door. Ring me a phone and I pick it up and ask who's there. Put a envelope in my hands and I open it without looking at who it's from.

Solomon stood in the doorway, wearing rain. "I'm looking for Lela."

"You found her."

"Is she all right? I want to talk to her."

This is 1934, remember, and a white woman in a black man's room is cause for murder. Lela was still holding that newspaper joint in her fingers, dragging hard on it, and ashes falling all over the floor.

"She's just fine, Solomon. Now, you go on home."

"It's her dresses," he said. "They aren't there. I looked in the closet and they're gone. And her shoes."

Lela said she was wearing her shoes.

Solomon said the other ones, the blue ones.

"Go home, man."

"But her dresses are gone."

Whenever I open the door on craziness, I close it as fast as I can. I asked Lela where her dresses were. Solomon was scratching on the door like some kind a dog.

"I took them to Harry's."

"Harry's who?"

"Harry Lord. He wrote me the song."

I made some more tea and smoked it myself for breakfast while Lela told me how she met Harry Lord. They'd been at the club during off hours and he'd just drifted in and asked if he could play with some of the irregulars who'd shown up for a jam. Later, he'd taken her home and played all his stuff for her, things I'd heard before and never had much to do with, all that sheet music piling up in his room and for I don't know how many years. I always figured if he'd put all those notes into a mattress he'd have a hell of a bed and still no career, but Lela thought otherwise.

"He's got a few troubles, I know. I don't even know if he can hear himself. We took this one song and it was full of slow stuff, an upward run and trickle down to key, it was like funeral music, but he let me play around with it till I was comfortable and he did everything I told him to do, like lift it up to two-four, drop the bass an octave, and hit it every *other* bar, just for an anchor. We played all evening till we had it down and it was a new song but the same one. It worked. So then we changed the lyrics. . . ."

That was the first time I heard "A Long Fall into Shallow Waters," when Lela sang it a capella, and if I didn't think much of it then it's mostly cause there was no piano and Lela's voice, great as it was, always needed that piano to cuddle into and to push off. Anyway, I was kind a surprised by the words, cause they reminded me of something Lela had once told me about herself, where she came from, some place in the Midwest. There was this boy who wanted to marry her, and when she said no he throwed himself off a bridge. She might a made that up, too, I don't know. Anyway, that's the song she sang, "A Long Fall into Shallow Waters," and it sure as hell wasn't Harry Lord who wrote the words.

We didn't hear Solomon scratching anymore and we figured he'd gone away, and that's when Lela told me all about him. His family had found out he wasn't going to school and was instead spending his time writing poems and following Lela around, so he got his money cut off and there wasn't much left except what was in his trust. He was only twenty and the trust wouldn't be his for another three years, but the sad part, Lela said, was that he wasn't sure he'd ever make it to twenty-three, cause he was sick, dying sick.

"That's why I've been staying with him. He knows I couldn't love him. I never slept with him, except once, out of kindness. He's got some disease, he says, something wrong with his blood. He says if I stay with him till the end he'll put the trust in my name. It would be mine when he . . . Don't look at me like that, Fingers. I only slept with him once. He said the money would be in my name and he just wanted to be with someone for the last few years."

Why I wanted to get helpless drunk. Desperate is. Now Lela was telling me she was in love with Harry Lord and though I didn't believe it at the time, writing it off to the rain and the marijuana and whatever, it turns out she meant it. She made something fine of his music and even though I never was much of a fan I knew plenty of others who swore by Lela Maar, who said she was a hell of an instrument, meaning more than how she could sing, and since I knew her before and after Harry I know as well how much of it was coming from him. Lela sitting in my rat-trap room, drinking tea while the rain dried in her hair, singing "A Long Fall into Shallow Waters," that may have been the beginning for her but all I saw was desperation, like I sometimes saw in that black face in the mirror, scared of not being, of staying forever in that half-empty nightclub and playing drunk some chord, over and over, can't resolve it. Lela in love with Harry Lord. After all, why not? If the music says so.

Around noon, with nothing left to smoke and me getting fidgety for a cigarette, no more rain to keep us indoors anyway, we counted our loose change and figured we had enough for both cigarettes and breakfast and there was still nine long hours to kill before going to the club. Solomon was still in the hallway, his head pillowed on folded arms, and we stepped over him like over a dead man, respectfully, and tiptoed down the stairway to the street.

"Long Fall . . ." got recorded by Black Dot and even sold pretty well but there was a couple a years more of hard times for Harry and Lela, playing the dip joints and pinballing around Manhattan looking for a full-time label. I didn't see too much a them for a few years. I was making my own success uptown and hangin around less with whites. I could tell you all kinds of stories about those years but I'd be just filling in with what I heard instead a what I saw.

During breakfast that morning Lela said she had to quit our gig. She was moving in with Harry, she said, and they were going to do some serious work, build up their own gig and try to make it to 52nd Street. We didn't know. We were high as kites from all the muggles and no sleep, Lela in love and me still drifting in my head the way I used to, we didn't know that Solomon woke up in front of that door and knew we was gone, that he was still wet all over from the rain, that he didn't really have no sickness but had said so just to find a way to keep Lela hanging around with him; that he wanted love worse even than we did. We didn't know he got up and went home, maybe thinking Lela'd be there like before, washing her dresses and underthings, working octaves and getting ready for the night's gig. Desperate for something I never put a name to but knew in my heart, he must a walked the streets for a long time before he got home. We didn't know how deep the water was, we was high and we didn't feel much that day. All our cool and care was somewhere else just then. Solomon got up off the floor, the rain still all over him, and he wandered the island till he got to his place, up around West 12th, climbed the stairs and shoved the key in the lock and Lela wasn't there, and we didn't know he'd kill himself just because there was no dresses in the closet, he said he was dying and we said, Who isn't, maybe he hanged himself just because he got home and there was no one there to sing for him anymore.

VISITATIONS

My habit was to work without a net. Don't ask why. I didn't plan on dying there. Blame it on superstition. Too many times if I'd had a gun I would have turned it on myself, so I walked around with this empty holster, a clear enough sign to anyone what a dangerous man I'd become. Now that I'm out of it I think back on my work and see how the lines were drawn in the dirt and how I went around erasing them. I was forever climbing deeper into that elephant's asshole to get a better look. The closer I got, the darker things became, so I made the logical move from color film to black & white.

I remember how the grunts used to go into the field with their Instamatics, Polaroids, whatever. After a firefight, they'd be snapping away at corpses, decapitated Cong, naked and pretzeled women, and those inevitable four-year-old soldiers shrapneled to oblivion. One Marine said he had a collection of hundreds of those pictures and once he got home he would show them to his friends and neighbors and we'd just see who messed with *him* anymore.

Whenever I'd get back to Saigon after a long spell up north, I'd do something crazy. Maybe it was to counteract the depression, the letdown.

I always felt that if I wasn't dead I should at least be a little chewed-on, some piece of me rotting in the clench of a dead man's teeth. My face or my ass. Washing my hair for the first time in a week, I scratched out bits of metal, shrapnel dust, and dead leaves. Something tasted like ashes but when I spit there was only whisky. Closing my eyes, I crossed a busy street, and when nothing ran me over I stepped into the first bar I could find, headed for the loo, and threw my face at the mirror.

I awaken, sensing myself being sniffed over, dog or derelict, but when I open my eyes I am alone. I can smell gunpowder but it makes no sense. Just another one of those things to fret over.

Rising, I take inventory of my knapsack. Film case, lens case, T-shirts, pills for sleep and pills for pain, French paperback, torn clothing; it's all there. "Lela Maar Sings Harry Lord." I couldn't listen to all of it in one go. It was too much for me and I fled the record shop after the pain set in and went searching out my x and y for the night, ending up off Houston Street in the prettiest little doorway this side of the Village. Sirens punctured my slumber throughout the night. Everyone was under arrest but me.

I'm walking stiff-legged, like some deadbeat, and my knee doesn't loosen up until I'm already in the East Village. Limping into a doorway, I order coffee and a hard roll and light a cigarette. There is a newspaper in front of me but I can't read the words. When I focus they seem to slide off the page. I realize by now it has nothing to do with that plate in my head. Six years of hanging around journalists was enough. They got tired of the lies themselves but there was little else to write, except in fiction. The body bags had to be counted, didn't they? And firefights termed as battles or engagements. Keeping those facts dry and safe from the monsoon of what must really have been happening. They did like me, finally. Took to drink and drugs and did their jobs. Photography as a way of closing your eyes. Writing as a way of shutting up.

"You want another cup?"

"Sure."

"You read about Nixon?"

"Who?"

"The president. I'll give him two more days. He can't hold out much longer."

"What's to hold out?"

"Watergate, man. Where you been?"

Good question, I'm thinking, stirring sugar into my coffee. Answers abound but I realize he doesn't really want to know. "You got a telephone?"

"Behind the register. Not a pay phone. I'll put it on your tab."

Needing some way to congratulate myself, I call my agent. He's been expecting me.

"You need help," he says.

"Just saying hello," I tell him.

"I assume you're back for good this time."

"It's a safe assumption."

"Then why don't I believe you?"

His name is Gabriel and he owes me money, royalties at the very least. My book is still in print and hasn't yet gone the way of bargain bins.

"They're beginning to think you're famous, Page. The man who opened Pandora's box. You bring anything back across with you?"

"More of the same. A picture window in my forehead."

"We heard that you were hit. Some of us were pulling for you."

"Not all of you?"

"Not everybody loves you, Page."

I thanked him for the very hot tip.

"I've been getting these phone calls, Page. Very polite but I can smell the menace. Someone in the army is looking for you. Making it sound like a minor matter."

"You haven't seen me and you haven't heard from me."

"I know the rules. But where can I find you?"

"If I knew, I'd tell you." I hang up.

If I could feel love like that, she'd be the love of my life. She and the boy can't make a family all by themselves. But when I smell myself there isn't a trace of that man I'm looking for. Whatever makes a father. Not that I haven't thought about it. Any woman I've ever come inside gets the once-over and I don't want to be careless. Not the way Lela was, with all her coming and going. She might have thought of me, just once. The least she could have done was keep a diary.

I call Jane's number and a stranger answers.

"She no here. She work."

"I get it. You're taking care of the baby."

"Hunter sleeping. You call later."

I wrangle the number of Jane's gallery out of her, in Spanish, then give it four rings before she answers.

"So where'd you sleep?"

"In the jungle, dreaming of you."

"That sounds like love, Page."

"I never said otherwise."

"So when will I see your face?"

"It's not all there anymore."

"Listen, Page. I'm not going to pity you, I'm going to take care of you."

I raise my fist and glance at my wrist but there's no watch there. I lost that, too, in the accident. "Meet me somewhere."

"Why not at home?"

"Whose home?"

"Funny man. Don't you ever worry that I'll get tired of your double-talk?"

"I'm serious. On neutral ground."

There is a pause, a measuring of intent. "Where, then?"

An hour later I am upriver, at Riverside Park, sitting on a bench with pigeons at my feet. Tipping my head backward, I wait for angels to come steal the pennies from my closed eyes. I pretend to sleep and then I do sleep for a minute or two and when I awaken I see Jane crossing the playground. She is wearing a yellow dress and I'm thinking how nice, her dark hair longer than I remembered it from over there. I didn't have her picture except beneath my closed lids.

When she sees me she doesn't wave. Simply tilts her head and comes toward me in what I imagine to be slow motion but actually it's the distance. Suddenly I don't want the words, the dialogue, anything resembling argument. I want only this vision of her coming toward me, but then she is there and I'm made to understand I should embrace her.

We kiss and it's a mere touching of lips and then she is looking at my forehead, trying to see what's missing. "I expected worse," she says. "Scars and bruises."

I tell her she's looking at my good side.

"Do we sit here or do we walk?"

We walk. Though it is almost noon the playground is nearly empty, an abandoned landscape of slide, jungle gym, teeter-totter, and sandbox. If Jane notices the limp she doesn't let on but all the same reaches a hand to my forearm; one of us is steadying the other.

She wants to know what I'll do now, what are my plans. "Is it over, your war?"

"That's what they tell me. I've been bounced, you might say. Like a bad check. Even before my jeep hit that mine, they didn't want me there anymore. I was getting to be like that black cat and they were very, very superstitious."

"You'll need a job."

"That's tomorrow's project."

"I was thinking of Hunter."

"So was I."

"He's a lovely boy. His eyes . . ." Her own eyes are like stones. She stops walking and faces me. "I have to tell you. Before he came, I was worried. About his eyes. It's cheap and racist, I know. Anyway, they're not."

"Not what?"

"Slanted. Oriental."

I tell her that the wealthy in Saigon often have surgery to remove the fold. "To become Western. It's considered a luxury."

"I didn't mean it that way. I'm sorry."

At 82nd Street we leave the park and I realize that we're only three blocks from Jane's place. I wonder if she's leading me there and remind her that I know my way around.

"I thought you'd want to see him."

I tell her it can wait. "I'm having these second thoughts."

She stops me dead on the street. "What do you mean?"

It occurs to me that I didn't bring flowers, a jewel, anything. Those kinds of gestures are foreign to me, or maybe I'm simply out of practice.

Jane is still looking at me. "Say it, Page."

"I'm trying."

"On your knees, if it will make you feel better."

That line gets me hot but I don't have a comeback.

"I've had him six months, Page. *Your* little Hunter. At first I didn't want him at all, I wanted you. When you didn't come back with him, I panicked. I tried to give him to my mother but she wouldn't have it. So I hired Teresa to take care of him and I kept my distance. It wasn't hard except at night, when he'd cry. I couldn't leave him like that. No woman could."

Taking her arm, I try to get her to walk. Downtown, away from her place. She holds her ground.

"When I heard you were wounded I had Hunter to comfort me. All these weeks. When the papers came for us to sign I decided I'd marry you, whatever the bogus reasoning was."

"Jane."

"You made me a mother, you bastard. Not like I wanted it, but it's done. Don't play dead on me now."

I ask her who's playing and she slaps me hard across the face.

"I didn't mean that, Page. I meant to hurt you, but I forgot about your head."

"All the king's horses and all the king's men. I'm not that fragile. I've had worse." But already I'm walking away from her.

"Where are you going?"

"Somewhere safe where I can think."

"When you're finished thinking I'll still be here."

I already know. She has a way of staying; which shitty irony for her forever gives me the courage to walk away.

*

At the track I lose ten dollars on a horse named Dog Eats All, an eight-to-one shot. I don't even like the races and tell myself I'm killing time before it kills me. Sitting in the bar after the third race, I order a double bourbon and hold it before me like hemlock. I haven't touched a drop since yesterday and my head is clear as a bell, a bad omen. I drink the bourbon down, grateful for the burning.

In the fourth race, I lay five dollars, a sucker bet, on a horse named Running Dog. It's my day for it at six-to-one. "Who you got?" an old woman asks me, and when I tell her she says to bet horses, not dogs. "You got the right track?"

Running Dog, with knees like mine, limps in last, and I scan the card for the remaining races. Finding no names with dogs, I wait for the seventh race to bet twenty dollars on Crossbones to win. When he does I feel as though I've won the war at five-to-one. A cheap war, without contact, but a war all the same.

Armand Page, my guardian, used to tell me that history mattered, that the past and the future are finally indistinguishable. That's why I had to know about my mother, he said. Who she was and how she lived.

"She won't be any help to you. Not now that she's gone. But you're lucky, Hunter. She was far from no one and there are books to read."

Her biographies, he meant. The stories of her years in oblivion before fame set in like a permanent fever. "You can't believe everything," Armand told me. "Sometimes these writers get stuck for sales and they make things up. And sometimes you'll have to fill in the blanks for yourself."

That was the beginning of the archives, these biographies and old magazines; those and the stacks of records Armand would gather from the shops. Reading all that was my pastime for a while. Others played stickball or raised kittens. Page built this mother temple in the name of history, memorizing the chronology of Lela Maar and pasting it all together in his mind like a neat collage with only one panel missing.

It's all still there, in a trunk in Jane's walk-in closet. Hardcovers and paperbacks, autographs, clippings from the *Times*, the *Herald Tribune*, and *Melody Maker*, a boxed set of stills of my mother at Carnegie Hall, sheet music, and a carton of her letters that Armand bid for when they held the auction.

I have my own version of the events but I've never written it. I've already invested too much in the knowing and doubt that words would say it. This much is clear, she didn't count on having me. She went to England for personal reasons, call it love or the need for it, but babies didn't qualify. The first act of my small life was to call her bluff. Years of doing it and she'd never been pregnant before. I must have been a shock.

Jane doesn't want my history, she says. She wants me. We're one and the same, I tell her, but she thinks otherwise. All that reading has screwed up my rhythm. Heading for tomorrow, I step in yesterday's dogshit.

More dog images. I swear I'm obsessed. When I step off the air-conditioned bus into that August heat, my lungs collapse like dimestore accordions. I've passed out again but it doesn't bother me now. I've been down before and I know the terrain. The light at the end of the tunnel is a foot on my hand and someone is saying from a distance: Get up, you bum.

I meet Gabriel at the Whistler for dinner. We are always making excuses about seeing each other, neither of us wanting to call it friendship, but *business* isn't the word that applies. He is worried about me, he says, and for the first ten minutes he doesn't take his eyes off my forehead. "It's barely noticeable," he says.

"Then why are you staring at it?"

"I was 4F," he explains. "Physically unfit. When I got the notice for my physical, I went into action. Drugs, chain-smoking, three days at a time without sleep, television till all hours of the night. Pushing my blood pressure into the ozone. Three times they checked me out and three times I got passed over. They knew what I'd done but they couldn't prove it."

"You could have gone to Canada."

"I don't like the cold. Anyway, I always assumed that if I went I'd get hurt bad. That's why your head is so interesting to me. As if you got what was meant for me."

I don't know what to say so I swizzle my bourbon and wait for the headache to set in.

Gabriel lays an envelope in my open hand, a quarter-inch of bills. "It's not all there," he says. "I didn't want to draw a check and this is all the cash we had lying around the office."

I ask why not a check.

"I'm looking out for your interests. I might be watched. They've called again and they know you're in New York."

"Who?"

"You keep pretending innocence. Your army friends."

"I don't have any friends, Gabriel."

"You're right, Page. You're too weird. This time I asked them what it's about and they said it's your pictures."

"Someone wants my autograph."

Gabriel sets down his knife. "You didn't tell me you were adopting a kid."

I tell him it hasn't happened yet, that it might be another rumor.

"Somehow I can't imagine you a father."

Why in hell not? I wonder, but I let it pass. Handing him a manila envelope, I tell him to open it. There are sixty-four frames inside, enlarged to eight by eleven. He gives each of them the once-over before putting them back in the envelope.

"Different," he says. "Unexpected, I guess. All this family business just when I was getting used to your headless babies. Who's the woman?"

"Chulin. She's dead."

"I was expecting more war pictures. Bombs bursting, dead people, horror, and such. That's been your signature."

"Maybe I've switched hands. There are families there, you know. We always have a way of forgetting that."

"No one's forgetting, Page. No one's interested, is all."

"Will you print them?"

Gabriel pours more wine for himself, notices that my glass is still full. "You don't drink like you used to. That head thing?"

"I asked if you'd print them."

"Don't get touchy. I don't mean to dodge you. But you know me, Page. I can't tell art from my asshole. I'll have to show them to some editors first."

"If you won't I'll take them elsewhere."

"That's your right. I'm just wondering what's possessed you."

"I'm trying to buy something back. Years of something. Print the pictures and I might rest a little easier."

Gabriel has another gift for me, a phone number. "Your guardian angels," he said. "They asked me to give you the number, that's all. I'm not saying you should call."

I'm feeling faint again but don't want to show it. Propping myself against the back of the chair, I reach for my glass but my hand misses. I want to say something final to Gabriel but when my lips move there is no sound. I mean to tell him about the order of the photographs, how they should be bound. Hardly chronological but not *méli-mélo* either. Start with that one of Chulin in the garden, raking up the dead birds. There's the shadow of a man behind her and I'm the only one who needs to know it's me, the sun wheeling up behind my hand and putting me there. After that, the black and white of Dune Buggy, asleep on the wet ground, dead palm fronds covering his face. The neighbors bent over their dinner table, hands reaching into a common bowl of wet rice. Hunter leaping head first from his mother's womb, Dune Buggy's hands poised to catch him. Or it doesn't matter what order, just print the damn things and let me out of here.

The feeling passes. I sip from my glass and feel my ass firmly on the chair. Gabriel is staring at me.

"I thought I'd lost you there. It's serious, isn't it?"

"The wounds have healed, Gabe. Ask for the check."

On the street he offers to give me a lift home but I tell him I haven't settled on an address.

"Do you plan on calling that number? They'll want to know."

"Whose side are you on?"

"My own. What did you do, kill somebody?"

"I don't remember. There isn't any evidence."

Meaning affection, he touches my shoulder. "Don't be a stranger."

I tell him I never meant to be.

From a booth at 86th and Broadway, I call Jane. It is past midnight and I assume I've awakened the baby.

"What is it?"

"I need the trunk."

"Page, do you know what time it is?"

I tell her I don't. "Late is all."

"You can come for it tomorrow. Teresa will let you in."

But it's not the entire contents of the trunk that I'm after. Just the letters. There are twenty in all, more than half of them written to her anarchist lover, Valentine. I haven't read them in years but the time seems right. You start pawing over the future and the past looks somehow immaculate and insoluble.

A VALENTINE DINNER PARTY

NEW YORK

1930

Valentine, a landlord despite himself, lives in the downstairs of his brownstone, and on Friday nights, like most nights, the anarchists come to his place to print their newspaper on the press in the basement, drink coffee, eat spaghetti, play his seldom-tuned piano, and discuss bombs and mobs and movements. As though the human world will turn on a phrase, a thought, a gesture of good intentions. His mother had bought the house more than ten years before, in 1920, just after Emma Goldman had been deported back to Russia. Valentine, now almost thirty, carries on without her, the son of a famous friend of a famous, if eclipsed, anarchist. He is sitting at the kitchen table going over proofs of *Forward Thinking*, a weekly rag he's been putting on the streets for the past few years, news and views from the New York underground now that the Crash has put protest back in business, the giddy decade laid to rest.

Woudner sits at his elbow and breathes upon the pages, telling Valentine again how a single bomb, well placed, impeccably timed, might ignite a revolution, if not a wholesale transformation of the species. He pushes his glasses halfway up his nose and edges his chair closer to the editor's, crowding him, nodding, smiling through his teeth. Elsa, her great bosom heaving, sits across from the two of them and corrects aloud a poem that Valentine has already twice rejected. "Why?" she wants to know.

"It's not swinish enough. Hearts and flowers. And rhyme."

It is a poem about passion and anarchy being mirror emotive forces but on different planes of recognition. Hard times for a love-hungry intellectual. First she had removed the rhyme but now she has added a line she finds both cruel and lovely and she recites it across the table to Valentine to see what he thinks:

My lover and my outlaw, first we dressed your God in black;
with a shovel, in the moonlight, we thus buried Him out back.

Woudner says, "One bomb ticking. Like a timepiece, toward destiny."

Elsa sets the pages on the table, awaiting Valentine's word.

"I thought you got rid of the rhyme."

"I did." She sighs, rather too prettily. "But the poem was too much for me without it."

As Elsa is too much without someone to shepherd her over the rough terrain of politics, journalism, loneliness, and occasional female itching. She watches Valentine across the table, seeking his eyes. *You are the man for whom I would lose weight; I would shed my clothes and my body fat for your love. . . .* She'd been a grade-school teacher, well placed, before the Movement (passion/anarchy) had found her with Woudner; had previously recited Emily Dickinson to the four papered walls and written her own verse for small magazines that never sold and could barely be given away. Her poems fell into the hands of old ladies who used them to line cat boxes, her verse shredded but at least useful.

To cheer her up—or to get her off his back—Valentine sends her to the corner Italian to buy wine. Sensible Jenny, a holdover from his mother's days in the Movement, has finished the spaghetti and is calling up the printers, Lalo and Eddie, from the basement, and bangs on the wall to quiet the wild-eyed Hammel, who has requisitioned Valentine's bed with Woudner's one-time sister-in-law.

The house is full of books and newspapers and magazines, unfurled posters from past rallies, notebooks, sayings pinned to walls, cigarette papers, catalogs, drafts of speeches, shredded poems. The place is flammable, the least spark could set it off, but Valentine just wants to get the paper out on time, so he goes on typing, correcting his essay incendiary phrase by incendiary phrase, replacing *justice* with *vengeance* and X'ing words that Woudner has classified as quasi-religious.

"Seriously, Val, one would think you were raised by a covey of Carmelites instead of the great Sarah Valentine. You have such a weakness for sanctimoniousness."

"That is not a word. Sanctimony, you mean."

"There. The proof. You are as much a slave to dictionaries as to dogma."

"Simple diction, Woudner. A want of clarity."

Woudner grins. "Language, to you, is a straitjacket. You should be writing bombs instead of well-honed homilies. There is more law and order in your writing than a courthouse. If I were editor . . ."

"We'd be in jail."

"Until the jails were overflowing and the prisoners outnumbered the lawful citizens. Inside would become outside. Think of it."

Jenny, wasting no words, gathers paper, pamphlets, pens, and pencils from the large table and shoves everything on top of the refrigerator. She is a small woman with the presence of a large one, her graying hair arranged into a crown atop her head. She tells Valentine to move his typewriter, she needs a space for the spaghetti. Lalo and Eddie, up from the basement, remove their ink-stained bibs and sit with blackened hands at the end of the table, Lalo saying the press is getting worn and he'll need some spare parts. "The roller, she don't roll so good and we's losing ink every other sheet. I can't get a folio without a double pass and you should see the blur we got on page two."

Valentine asks him how much and notes the amount in a little black book he keeps in his breast pocket.

Hammel and the woman, Sylvia, join them at the table and Woudner passes them the bread. Hammel, like Woudner, is new to the group, and although he has an enthusiasm some of the others are lacking, Valentine distrusts him. He is a petty anarchist rather than a principled criminal, and is fond of breaking windows, lighting fires, and bashing heads. A soldier. When he'd first come to the brownstone he'd thought himself at the communist bureau. When advised otherwise, he'd merely shrugged and said, "Same difference." And stayed.

Lalo, who has strong hands and a slow mind, opens a bottle of wine with a bent fork and they all begin to eat with appetites that no longer surprise Valentine. When his mother bought the house he asked why so many rooms and she said, "You'll see. Anarchy is part action and part dinner party. One precedes the other, continually."

But even the anarchists are unable to sit all together at the same table. Across town somewhere, in a basement or an apartment house, are the saboteurs, the nihilists, knife-wielders, and explosives experts with palms smelling of gasoline. These people write nothing on paper, remain nameless, and stay hidden, letting their histories be told by rubble and broken glass. What is left to Valentine are the letter-writers, the pamphleteers, the marchers, professors, poets, and disillusioned émigrés, the few who have joined in what remains of Sarah Valentine's optimistically named American Anarchist Alliance.

They are planning something noisy, a burst of some kind to rescue their identity. Enrollment is down and action is called for. Valentine is sorry that more of them haven't shown up tonight. Normally Jack would be there, and Eleanor and Walter. Valentine can't always shut Woudner up, not alone. They want to see results, his thirty followers, and although a headache blooms behind his eyes whenever one of them suggests arson or vandalism, he understands their impatience; he feels it himself.

On the 14th of October an alliance of labor groups, socialists, communists, and agrarian reformers are planning a mass rally and march, starting at Union Square and snaking upward through the belly of Manhattan to its heart, Central Park. All of the exiled and jobless, the illiterate and unwashed, have been invited, even to the splinter groups, feminist committees, riff and raff, but the anarchists, radical black sheep of the resuscitated movements, have been snubbed. "Let's face it," a man tells Valentine. "Except for a few minor intellectuals, disgraced professors, and misguided Italian zealots, what can you bring to the Movement? To this point we've only seen chaos."

Valentine does what he has always done, by rote: distributing pamphlets, meeting with the faithful in various evil-smelling basements (though there is, on West 10th Street, the occasional smell of baking bread, sweet, from the shop above them), handing out sandwiches to new émigrés (kindness and bribery), visiting labor leaders to plead his fragile case, raising money among the fringe neighborhoods, and arguing into the dead of night with monied politicos who usually end up begging for mercy and pointing to the time. His ideas, inherited from his mother, are tinted sepia with age. Valentine feels he is tapping with a blind man's white-tipped cane on the brick wall of her hopes for him, and in the bottom of his heart he is not a believer but a disbeliever.

Dinner is nearly ended when Walter arrives. He stands in the doorway brushing rain from his sleeve. "Cats and dogs out there. And there's a cop across the street."

Valentine, relieved to see his levelheaded friend, offers him the seat next to his own. Jenny asks where's Eleanor.

"Making money," he answers. Walter is Eleanor's husband, a fact that everyone but Jenny forgets from time to time. The marriage has grown fragile under the weight of free love; every woman is every man's wife, as the saying goes. Walter believes in crowds with faces, not faceless crowds. "She's taken a night job at the hospital," he tells them, a convenient lie since they already know she's been working as a prostitute for weeks. "She won't be round till after midnight."

While Jenny clears the table, Lalo opens another pair of wine bottles and the planning begins. Jack arrives with fifteen dollars he's made from selling pamphlets and old books and he lays it on the table before Valentine, gathering congratulations.

"Where'd you really get the money?" Valentine whispers.

"The enemy's wallet," Jack tells him.

"We have no enemies, Jack."

"Wise up, Val. Take a look around."

Valentine notes the amount in his black book and hands the money to Jenny, who puts it in a metal box. The room grows uncomfortably warm with the windows shut to the rain, and the urgency of voices back and forth across the table.

We need funds.

There are ways to convince the unknowing.

Eh, listen to me, Lalo, we could cordon off the street, stop the rally ourselves. . . .

Woudner to Valentine: I know a man who deals in explosives, small and large.

My right to my words.

Jack: With more funds we could expand the newspaper, hire a professional editor, become more visible.

My right to anger and to violence.

Woudner to Valentine: Do you remember the bomb they found at Penn Station, in the black bag on Platform 6?

(Valentine, revising his editorial, feels suddenly lightheaded; the warmth of the room, the wine. He finds himself listening to Woudner instead of the others.)

An *anonymous* bomb, without a target, no one special in mind, not like an assassination . . .

My right to kick your teeth in.

. . . random death, inexplicable. The irremediable opening of the artery.

Jenny finds a comfortable chair in a far corner of the room and takes out a book, something smuggled from France, no title and filled with printing errors. She reads in smoky lamplight, comfortable in the center of the chaos. The universe is all that moves, turning round and round her. As she reads she can hear Woudner's voice, though the tones are soft, almost muted, above the others. Sarah Valentine, rest her soul, would have thrown that man out right now. Right out into the rain. Heel to toe, she would have. Her son, sitting there with his black book and no inspiration. A good man but a bad anarchist. She remembers an argument from many years ago, one man a writer and the other an assassin. "Words are my action," the writer had said. "Action is my action," replied the assassin. Valentine seeks to convince with his writing, to raise both cash and Lazarus. Woudner, she sees from a short distance, is the assassin. With one hand he raises the dead and with the other he blackjacks them back into oblivion.

Doors open and close and empty bottles are lined along the table like a firing squad. There are plans and counterplans but already the conversations have gone elsewhere, astray of the point: What *was* the point? Valentine wonders, noticing Hammel's hand on Sylvia's narrow back. Lalo and Eddie return to the basement with Valentine's editorial to finish the edition. Sylvia yawns, but no one notices, so she yawns again. Roger drops by with Olivia in tow, ex–drug-dealer and ex-prostitute, now running a halfway house for winos down near Battery Park. "Where are the others?"

Valentine realizes that there are no others, only these few.

Sylvia bids them all good night just as Gregory and what's-her-name arrive, and that brute who wants to be bodyguard to Valentine. Woudner takes him off into a corner, puts a glass into his hand, and talks directly into his ear.

The rain lets up and Walter cracks open a window, saying aloud that he wonders what's keeping Eleanor. But we all know, Walter. You know we know, so why play-act? In an open marriage there are no secrets, no wondering, and every act is Act One.

Hammel says he's turning in, g'night all, and, Val, don't forget to wake me at seven.

Jenny turns a page with thumb and moistened forefinger.

Walter, still at the window, says, "Someone's here. Someone's coming up the steps."

Lalo, up from the basement, is playing the piano, leaving ink all over the yellowed ivory keys.

Somehow, voiced if not voted upon, there is a plan. Since they are not invited to participate in the march, the anarchists will stop it. A barricade or two will have to be planned, and they are considering First Avenue, near 16th or 17th, allowing no detours, forcing a single file of humanity to step on its own heels and double backward.

"It's her," Walter says, disappointed.

Not Eleanor but Vera. There is a remnant of rain on her shoulders and in her hair, and her blue dress clings to her hips, damp and tight. She says a round of hellos, lifts a glass of wine and drinks from it, bends to kiss Jenny's cheek, then circles the table to Valentine, who puts his Manhattan street map aside to lay a kiss on her painted lips. "How'd it go?"

"Not bad." She pours herself more wine. "They let me sing the last two numbers, my own stuff, and the band was fine fine fine. Then the place closed up but I stayed for a drink with the piano player, who's really something to listen to, I mean when he talks. Is that all there is?" Pointing to a half-empty bottle of wine. When Valentine nods, she pours another. "Rain," she says. "Rain, rain. His name is Lester Mink but everybody calls him Fingers. A real strange talker."

She is starry-eyed, Valentine is thinking. No, her eyes are vacant, nothing recognizable swimming in her irises. Saying good night to one and all, she heads down the hall, opens a door and sees Hammel and Sylvia entwined and shivering in darkness, closes the door and goes into another, Valentine following. She shrugs out of her dress and takes a long time smoothing it over with her fingers, caressing away the rain and wrinkles, then she hangs it lovingly over the headboard, her blue dress, her nightclub dress. The bed is covered with uncollated pages of *Forward Thinking*, Lalo's unfinished work, and when she sweeps them onto the floor Valentine stoops to gather them, putting pages 1/2 and 7/8 into proper stacks along the wall, seeing at a glance what Lalo means about the blur on page 2: there are no words at all, only printed insects. Vera stretches naked across the bed, seems to sleep.

"Do you need anything?" he asks her, thinking she might be drunk, or is it something else? What does she do at night? She never tells him all of it. Her body, in the half-dark, excites him, but he knows the others will be waiting for him. They have to decide upon a location for the barricade, battle positions, contingencies. He is about to leave her when she suddenly sits up and rummages through her purse for cigarettes, finds one and lights it, reclines again.

"Vera, I have to . . ."

"I meant to tell you. I'm not Vera anymore. I changed my name tonight. Lela. What do you think?" As though a dress, a pair of mother-of-pearl earrings. "Lela Marsh."

"I don't know."

"See, that's what Fingers called me. That piano player. He thought my name was Lela and he called me that all night. Even introduced me to the sixteen people left in the place when I finally got up to sing. 'Lela *Mars*,' he said. A funny kind of man."

"Sleep now. You're tired. I have to get back to the others."

"Tomorrow is Friday?"

"Today is Friday. Was. Tomorrow's Saturday."

"They want me back, Val. They want me to sing with them."

"Who?"

"Fingers and his group. They need a singer and I guess I pass."

"Good for you, Vera."

"*Lela*."

"OK. Lela."

"Come back later and make love to me. Even if I'm sleeping. Wake me up. You know."

"I will."

He turns to go, wondering how long until he'll be back with her.

"Val?"

"Lela?"

"Help me find a last name. Lela has to go with something other than Marsh, don't you think?"

"No. I don't know. A name is a name."

"Not true. A name is a language and it has to say something to you. Hurry and come back to me. I need you tonight."

I need you every night.

The door closes on the singer searching the dark for a name to follow her name. Marsh, Mars, Mara, Maar.

Sarah Valentine, for all anyone knew of her, might have been the Virgin Mother. Something had to explain her son; babies are not conceived of thin air or a glass of Burgundy or a wish upon a fragile star. A lifetime anarchist and close friend of Emma Goldman's, she had never been seen with any man one might have described as a lover, a paramour, or a bedmate. There were lesbian networks among the turn-of-the-century crowd, lavender-papered rooms where politics dissolved like a grainy film into closed curtains, whispering, release, and an epidemic of patchwork marriages, individually defined among artists and activists like a deck of cards with faces only, queen on king, queen on queen, the king of hearts sidling over to the queen of spades and she saying she believes in lavender rooms, look elsewhere. But Sarah's name was never linked to any of the stories, gossip or truth, of those unruly times. She was a scholar, a writer, a worker, far removed from the pollen and the perjury of love, loving, lovers.

She might have been purposefully pregnant, a clinical coitus somewhere out west for the sake of family continuity, but she didn't believe in the concept of family, which she once wrote to be a "tribal tyranny." Or had there been, in the deep recesses of her anarchic soul, a spark of eroticism, just enough to fan into flame, once? Or there was rape, a calamitous alleyway, a misstep into someone's darkness.

In any case there was him, her son, proof of pregnancy, neither ecstatic nor hysterical.

They had first lived in Brooklyn, not far from Ebbets Field, in a house kept up with inherited money. When Alexander—he hated the name and went by Val—had been ten, they'd moved into Manhattan, taking over the ground floor of a brownstone. Sarah had bought the printing press and gone back into the business after a decade of tamely raising her son, of reading and reflecting, and keeping up with the frenetic activity of her friend Emma Goldman. She had read Johann Most's *Science of Revolutionary Warfare* and been horrified, and had been even more troubled by Emma's complaisance regarding violence as a necessity. Stilettos, pistols, alcohol bombs, and broken bottles were, as they were telling her, fluent in their own languages. By the time Emma was deported in 1919, Sarah Valentine had already been relegated to the back of the anarchist ranks, considered eloquent but toothless, her wisdom flawed with the rust of compassion. Flawed? she sang to the ceiling, to the walls, to her gaping son. Her faith in the others, in what they were up to, had been suddenly under new scrutiny. Her first tract on the new press, a simple folio entitled *Arrogance and Anarchy*, had gotten her thrown out of the Anarchists Union when she'd refused to soften the lines: "They wish to see the end of the struggle in their own lifetimes, these snipers and firebugs, as though history is but a short, straight line from beginning to end, as if we are destined to arrive at a cataclysm, an apocalypse, a coda. In their haste for a new order, they ask us to hurry the end of this one and to shoot our own children in our crossfire." Assassins. Mad bombers. Snipers. Fanatic *anything* is criminal. Ten years of raising a son had taught her the swiftness of passing time. In the interim, she had become a relic, a useless pioneer, and eventually the spearhead of an all-too-minor schism in the Movement. She had been put upon a wall and revered.

When she'd died in her sleep in 1925, by which time word of the Bolshevik betrayal had begun to trickle back to America, they had all come to her funeral, and someone there had read a letter of eulogy from Emma, and a number of featureless men in rumpled overcoats had stood off to one side, nervously copying down names.

If government is No, the limited, then anarchy is Yes, the limitless. She said this, but she also said that black and white were the same color, the only things a blind man can see. She said that every day is a history unto itself, don't look for patterns, there are too many of them and any combination of them can be used to justify madness. Living is by its nature an inexact science and only spontaneity is a sure bet.

She and Lela would have really hit it off, Valentine is thinking, as the singer, awakened, throws open her legs to him, saying "Maar. Lela Maar. Maar with two a's."

No lover of time, Valentine, there is always too little of it, or too much, an unwieldy sack of rocks he has to haul continually from one place to another, and when he arrives the sack is empty, his jewels slipped through a hole in the bottom, paving in glitter the road behind him, nothing left to pave the way ahead. Two new anarchists replace the three who dropped out, the press breaks down and is repaired with donated parts, the machine of minor history slips and unslips its unoiled joints, loosened bolts, parts rusting in the rain, work becoming trash becoming art. . . .

He and Vera first met on a street where he was distributing free leaflets, *The Truth About Anarchy*. She was out of work, looking hard for a job, and she took a stack of leaflets to cover her head from the rain, saying she supposed it didn't make any difference, she was already soaked to the skin and just look, nobody's reading your leaflets anyway.

He answered, "No matter. That's why they're free. One in ten might be read. One in a thousand might be answered."

"Answered? Like a prayer or a want ad?"

"Something like that."

He had hired her to help him distribute and they had climbed Manhattan parallel to each other, he on Eighth Avenue and she on Seventh. She needed a place to stay, she said. "More than money, I need a bed to sleep in." So he had brought her home to his brownstone, introducing her to Jenny ("Your mother? Your nurse?" "My cook and confidante") and putting her in the empty room next to his. In the middle of the second night she had come into *his* room, asking for cigarettes, a glass of water, something to read. "Or I won't make excuses for either of us and just stay."

"It's a large bed. Choose your corner."

For a week they had distributed leaflets in the day and slept side by side at night, untouching, Vera asking him one night, "Is this what they mean by comrades? I thought we were friends." She wanted to be a singer, she said, and occasionally she went off for long night hours, putting on a blue dress and applying makeup borrowed from Jenny. "I can't say I'm wild about her colors." Out into the dark to listen to bands, pick up tips, mingle, show off her voice.

The news of the world. A billion deutsche marks for a potato and free apples at Times Square. Businessmen falling like leaves from October trees out twenty-story windows, grasshoppers like Chinese armies obliterating Dakota cornfields. The softened face of Herbert Hoover, those tiny eyes peering out at Valentine from the pages of the *Herald Tribune*. All Vera wanted was to sing, while Val struggled under the weight of his alliance. The plumbing of the brownstone had burst and the upper-story tenants called on the law for recompense; water in the hallways or seeping yellow stains along the ceiling he watched, while his last cigarette burned slowly downward like a fuse toward his lips. The anarchist thought it over and still Woudner was wrong, fanatic anything is criminal, but the old man kept pushing, pushing, and some of them, though he wasn't sure who, were beginning to listen. Vera slept uneasily at his side those first nights, shifting her hips under the covers, undulating the mattress; he even suspected that sometimes she was masturbating, but didn't have the courage to see for himself, yes or no, and his phallus, hardened, was distracting, something had to be done about Woudner and those leaky pipes, she sang a single note, must have come of her own fingers, she slept and then he slept, leaflets to pass out tomorrow, we'll go farther uptown where there's less money and more hope, answered like a prayer.

One September morning, passing the last of his stack to a cripple meandering past, he crossed Columbus Circle to look for Vera, who usually had leaflets left over, she spent so much of her time wandering up and down the street, looking in windows at things she would later buy, dresses, shoes, jewels, when the day came. Stepping across Broadway, he hesitated, his eyes catching something in the gutter, wet words signed in his own hand. Stooping, he retrieved a leaflet, then another, and twenty more stuck wetly together. Up and down the street there were another hundred, and at the top he found the reason: they had been stuffed into the drain at the corner but had stopped it up, and the flowing water had carried them down the gutter. How many days had she done this? From the beginning?

"Where is Woudner and his bomb when I need them?"

He found her in a bar at the corner, putting money in a jukebox, head bobbing from the day's first drink. There was a man on either side of her, hands circling her waist, fingers clenched above her belly.

"Vera!" He stood at the opposite end of the bar, a clutch of leaflets in his hand, shaking them in the air.

Her eyes, porcelain-blue, looked into his. "Val, you're here." No surprise and no guilt. They'd been expecting each other.

"I found these. Outside. In the gutter."

"It was too much for me. I couldn't keep it up. No one reads them anyway. I didn't think you'd find out."

"It's my work, Vera."

"Val, don't."

He crossed the bar and took her by the arm. "We're leaving."

She said she wanted to stay. "Rainy days don't do me, Val. Listen to me." Gesturing to one of the men with her, she said, "This is Cliff. The other one, I don't know."

"Andrew," the man told her.

"They're out of work," Vera added.

Cliff stepped in. "Leave her alone if she wants to stay."

Valentine, for no reason, swung his fist in a wide semicircle, over Vera's upturned face, catching Cliff in the neck, a painful blow if not a solid one. There was a moment of immobility, a freeze, as if the film had stopped dead, an ominous whirring coming from somewhere. Then Andrew held Valentine while Cliff tom-tommed him, doubling him over, and the two of them dragged him to the door and out, depositing him on the sidewalk. Long moments later, as yet another rain began to fall, he sat up, patted his pockets for a hanky, his money, the keys to his house. All of me is still here. Vera was shouting above the jukebox but he couldn't hear the words, he held no more hope for her, she would never be an anarchist. The rain fell harder, in windy sheets, and he rose, brushing the front of his shirt, afraid to look underneath, where later, surely, there would be bruises.

He walked. One leg seemed to advance less than the other and he veered constantly to the right, out of alignment. He was nearly to Times Square by the time Vera caught up with him, wordlessly taking his arm and leading him into a taxi. He wouldn't look at her until they were home. The rain had covered her dress and the hem was splattered with mud, all of her mascara running down her face like gray elongated teardrops, her eyes two fine purgatories. She didn't say a word, she didn't need to, he wasn't blind and could see how sorry she was.

When they were together in the bathtub the hot water ran out, as always, and Valentine went into the kitchen to boil water. When he returned she was reclining in the tub, her feet dangling over the edge, her face cleared of makeup, eyes glistening.

"I couldn't do it," she said. "I'm not like you."

"What am I like?"

"You believe in what you do."

"Doesn't everyone?"

"Of course not. Take me."

He had never seen her naked in daylight, and the water, clouded with soap, seemed to magnify her breasts, her belly, that patch of hair.

"I do what comes easy to me. Whatever I can get by with."

His erection came to him silently, without trumpets or a knock on the door. "Not with your singing," he answered. "I've heard you."

"Were you moved?"

"Very much so. I knew you'd never be an anarchist. You live within yourself. You are your own religion and politics."

"I can sing. I really can. But no one knows it."

"I do."

She rinsed her breasts and he trembled. "But you're not a nightclub owner or an impresario."

"I'm only a revolutionary dealing in hopeless causes."

"I should have been your cause."

He didn't get it.

"I mean, you might have dedicated yourself to me. That's all any woman wants from a man. You write your pamphlets and you dig around looking for votes and signatures and holding rallies and having meetings. Spend that same energy on a woman and see where it gets you."

He still didn't understand and said so.

To show him, she stood up and the suds and water fell away from her body, slipping from her shoulders and breasts, dripping from her thighs.

"I'll show you," she said.

In the bedroom she pushed leaflets and books and letters and newspapers and coffee cups and pencils from his bed, and when there was nothing there but mattress and bedsheet, pillow and pillowcase, man and woman, she showed him.

They are assembled, grown men and women, for a dry run by night, at the end of an alley low down on the island. An Italian neighborhood, sprinkled with Czechs, Turks, and Hungarians, an Eastern salad of musics coming from the yellow windows that surround them while Valentine whispers signals into the fray.

It is only a simulation. They can't afford to build real barricades twice. When Valentine gives the signal for action, players leap from doorways, from behind trash bins, from crooks in sagging walls, hauling (imagined) planks, (invisible) barbed wire, (pretend) furniture, and Lalo, driving a (real and stolen) Packard up the street, meets Eddie in his car, the two simulating a minor crash (here Valentine imagines that the weight alone of the two cars will firm up the barricade) and leaping from the cars they race to join the others. Two terrified winos emerge from a back corner, hands over their heads, saying, Don't shoot, we ain't armed, don't even got no sneaky pete back here. Walter whistles a low note. "Pretty convincing, eh, Val?"

Phase one has taken three minutes and twelve seconds. On Valentine's signal, they simulate the second phase, a fallback to the side streets and two smaller barricades, with garbage-throwers on the rooftops. The strategy is Jack's and the execution is left to Valentine. When the second phase is timed at two minutes and forty-five seconds, Valentine signals for everyone to come in, they've done very well.

Lalo brings along the winos who want to join up. "They need to eat," Lalo says, "and they can help us throw the garbage off the roof."

Back at the brownstone, Jenny packs sandwiches while Valentine and the others rehearse once again the chronology. Pushing aside dinner leftovers, Valentine copies the map out three times and distributes the copies to Walter, Gregory, and Jack. "Anybody seen Woudner?" No one has. "He has the original of these maps. I'd rather he weren't out loose."

Elsa opens her mouth to speak, then thinks better of it.

Jenny says good riddance. "Sarah would have sent him packing, she . . ."

Walter suspects he's gone back to his radical friends, the undergrounders. "Didn't you know those guys, Hammel? Maybe you'd know how to contact him?"

Hammel says he hasn't seen them in more than a year.

Sylvia says, "But last week you . . ."

"It doesn't matter," Valentine concludes. "We can get by without him."

Vera, now Lela, comes in at the front door, her smile radiant as always at 3:00 a.m. after a gig with Fingers. A smoked something in her eyes. Isn't life painless? Lays her coat over an armchair and leans to kiss Valentine. The others, silent, watch her as they would an alien or a cop, waiting for her to leave. Of all of them, only Jenny says hello, though Sylvia nods shyly in her direction.

"We're almost finished, Lela. If you want to go to bed, I'll be there soon."

"No hurry. I think I'll stay. Maybe I can help."

Hammel says he doubts it.

"This isn't a nightclub," Eleanor adds. Her smile is unbalanced, the new bruise poorly camouflaged by powder above her lip, love Walter.

"No pianos, no liquor"—the first words from Olivia in more than an hour.

"And not a single lady in the audience," Jenny shuts them up.

Lalo lugs a crate of empty wine bottles up from the basement. Setting it on the floor, he tells Hammel there's another two crates down below, how many does he want?

"This'll do. Where's the gasoline?"

Woudner has the map. What if he's serious about his anonymous bomb, his random death letter? By the time Valentine looks up, Hammel has filled half a dozen bottles with gasoline and Lalo is helping him stuff the ends with old rags.

"No bottle bombs, Hammel."

The man straightens his back, looking the leader in the eye. "It's for effect, Valentine. Just for effect."

"Forget it. We start a fire, any fire, if we so much as light a match, the whole thing's over. Anarchy and arson don't mix, whatever Woudner says."

"Woudner isn't here."

"Precisely. He isn't here. And if he were he'd be for a full-scale holocaust, complete with cake and candles."

Jenny interrupts them. "What's this about a birthday party?"

"It's been canceled."

"Oh. Too bad."

"Lalo, take those bottles back down to the basement and empty the gasoline down the drain."

Elsa, rising to open a window, stands where she can see down the basement stairs to where Lalo has carried the bottles. Pretending to fidget with the curtains, she glances downward, seeing clearly where the bottles, still full to the brim, are stored behind the print plates, the Italian deftly laying a pair of letter boards across the top, shielding them from view. Woudner is gone; he is back with his wife and some kind of ragged army; no one in her bed these long nights. She opens wide the window and a wet breeze dampens her face. Lalo turns on a basement spigot, he's not so stupid, allowing for those glug-glug sounds Valentine will be waiting for. The threat of fire drained away, coordinates standing firm, chain of command intact. Elsa believes in the man but mostly she believes in men. Lalo stomps a bit too loudly up the steps—"All done, Val. Them bottles're empty"—and throws a glance too heavy to go unnoticed in the direction of Hammel, who sees Elsa, from her corner by the window, watching.

In bed with Valentine, a cigarette propped between her teeth, Lela says she's coming along.

"What's this?"

"I said I want to be there. With you and the others." When he doesn't answer she says, "Don't you want me?"

"The dangers are too obvious. If the police . . ."

"Sylvia's coming."

"That's different. She's one of us."

"Like hell. She's just along with Hammel."

Valentine takes the cigarette from between her teeth, drags on it, returns it. "You're wrong. Sylvia's sincere. She believes."

"So do I. I believe in Valentine."

"That isn't enough."

"Love, Val, not politics. When I'm in love, I don't measure my words, I don't consider what I say before saying it. In your politics, this anarchist thing, you choose a word for everything and everything you say runs parallel to what your heart says. Same direction but different goals. What if you get arrested?"

"I'll go to jail, like Woudner says is my duty. You'll come visit me with . . ."

"But I wouldn't. I'm not like that."

"Like what?"

"Faithful or devoted. At least not to someone who isn't there."

"Jenny would be here for you."

"I don't love Jenny. Jenny doesn't make love to me at night and I don't want your love in the abstract, in letters. If ever you're gone . . ."

"Don't say it, I think I already know."

"I wish you didn't. I try so hard to lie."

"You wouldn't wait."

"Weeks? Maybe. But never years."

"You wouldn't marry me. We wouldn't have children."

"I'm no one's mother. I'm everyone's wife."

"Eleanor said that."

"And I never forgot it."

"She was talking about herself."

"And I read it, *me*." She ignites the darkness with a match, letting it burn to the tips of her fingers, but the flame extinguishes itself before burning her. "That's a test, you know. Superstition. I do that every night before singing. If the match burns me, it means I'll do badly. The pain. Fingers taught me that, he knows all kinds of things. If the flame goes out, I'll be OK. This match says I'm going with you. Tomorrow. There's nothing to worry about."

"What if I said I was afraid for us? Something strange is going on here. . . ."

"I'd say we only have a few hours."

"Until what?"

"Until dawn."

"I don't think I can sleep. Shall we?"

Lela stretches like a shadow over his body. "I'll be on top."

Elsa, thinking herself alone in the kitchen, turns to find Hammel blocking her path to the refrigerator. He is a tall man and she is a short woman. Looking up at him is somehow painful at a close distance.

"One question," he says. "How much have you seen and how much do you think you know?"

"That's two questions, Lawrence," rolling his Christian name into two fruity syllables.

"Just answer."

She reaches around him for a cracker, snaps it between her teeth. "Where is Woudner?"

Hammel says he's gone back to his wife.

The ex–grade-school teacher feels a delicious calm come over her.

She is mistress of the scene, something rare and exhilarating. Usually she is the victim, her hands clasped before her, praying for whatever she wants rather than demanding it. "I already know he's gone back to his wife," she says. "But where?"

Hammel says he doesn't know. "He calls me, I don't call him." He takes the rest of the cracker from her hand, drops it to the floor, turns it into powder with his shoe. "Did you see Lalo?"

She steps backward, the better to look at him without craning her neck just so. "Yes, I saw him. He put letter boards over the box. Your body bombs or whatever are intact, *n'est-ce pas*?"

"*Bottle* bombs. Have you told Valentine?"

"Not yet."

"What's keeping you?"

Her hand reaches between his legs, tracing a finger up and down his length. "Woudner taught me this. He called it 'The Butterfly.' A very *slow* masturbation, much better performed when naked."

"You're not serious?"

She removes her hand. "What are you planning, Lawrence? A revolution or a murder?"

He hestitates, continuing to grind the cracker under his foot. Finally he says, "OK, we'll go down to the basement. There's a cot in the back room."

"Tut, Lawrence. Never in the basement. In your bedroom."

"But Sylvia's there. She's sleeping."

Her hand repeats the butterfly. "Delicate. Slow. Wake her up, Lawrence. She can sleep in my bed."

They leave the kitchen together, passing Lalo in the hallway, Hammel putting his finger to his lips, Elsa whispering, "Bring the Italian along, I might like it better that way."

Hammel curses, calling the name of some god in vain, whispers his trouble to Lalo, who nods and smiles and nods again, then he raises a hairy fist to knock Sylvia into wakefulness.

*

The night Woudner joined the Alliance, he explained his farsightedness to Valentine as though in answer to some question from an entry exam, What do you see of the world? "I require distance. Face to face with you, I can distinguish no particular features, nothing I would later call recognizable. Place yourself across the room and I will see you in all your surroundings, to the last detail of button and pocket, wrinkle and frown. But there's one more aspect." He removed his thick glasses, polished them with the tablecloth, and put them back on again. "I am also dichromatic, or, as simpletons put it, color-blind. Dichromatism is an extreme. I see two shades of the same color, nothing more."

"What color?"

"That's just it. I can't even tell you. Blue, aqueous on royal, sulphur on ocher, gray on black, you tell me. Elsa chooses my clothes for me in the morning. She tells me that my shirt is white and my slacks are brown. Does the tie meld chromatically with the ensemble? Are my shoes in harmony with my sleeves? There is no way for me to know. But when I close my eyes, I see the common color, the shade of all privacy. You will find that I prefer darkness to light, night to day. Give me an order, Valentine, and I will carry it out to the letter. I don't suffer from the confusions of most men."

In the course of a year, their relationship had caused them mutual grief. Multichromatic Valentine tended to his ambiguities, allowing for evolution and the right of those around him to refuse his ambitions. Woudner, chafing at him like a fine and incessant sandpaper, sought to wear through the skin of his humanity, to expose every last ganglion of rage, to alarm him. Once, Valentine had sent Woudner to the CPA headquarters to ask the communists for relief funds for seven jailed anarchists. Woudner was refused the money, of course, recent relations being what they were, and so, before returning to the brownstone, he'd gathered Lalo, Hammel, and a few others, gone back to the headquarters, and smashed windows, pillaged files, and threatened a secretary with Lalo's rusty machete. Horrified at this news, Valentine had hurried across Manhattan to make amends but had found no one to whom he could deliver his apology. When he returned home to the brownstone, he found the communists had already been there, leaving chaos behind.

"You see, Val, we are *not* of the same mind, we and the communists. They have to learn that we will step over their corpses into the future." His eyes, through the lenses, had been large and troubling and exacting. "Do you see this, Valentine? Is this clear to you?"

I should have thrown him out right then, Valentine considers, sitting up in bed. That should have been the end of him, so why didn't I do it?

Lela stirs, opens one eye. "Is it time?"

A shaft of light, a mingling of blue and gold and red and green, filters between the curtains to the bed. A rainbow for the crusades or a multichromatic dawn. Valentine rises, reaches for his pants. He would like to smoke a cigarette or roll the dice, something to put off, if only for a moment, this hard rising. But there are no cigarettes and no dice on the nightstand. He'll have to fend for himself.

Already he can hear Jenny in the kitchen, fussing over breakfast, anarchic clanging of pots and pans and silverware, Lalo's unmistakable boots up and down the basement steps, someone weeping, or laughing, in the next room, probably Sylvia again. "It's time," he tells Lela, but when she rises and sits on the edge of the bed, the sight of her reaching for her dress undoes him and he collapses to her side, taking her in his arms, kissing her forehead, her neck, her lips. "Val? . . ." But he doesn't want to speak to her or even to look at her. He wants to hold her back, like time preserved, and he does, for a long, long while.

Sylvia, adjusting the pillow behind her, Elsa's fat pillow, lights one cigarette with another.

Smoking away the blues. If I could sing like Lela, what notes would I be hearing just now? Then she is weeping, her tongue catching the salt at the corner of her mouth. She feeds herself with her sorrows.

She can hear the others stirring in the brownstone, Jenny trooping up and down the hallway, knocking on doors. "Elsa? Are you awake?" The old woman opens the door, sees Sylvia, says, "Oh. Um." Closes the door and carries on.

Already dressed, never undressed since being awakened by Hammel, she has only to put on her makeup, but there is just Elsa's awful white powder and too-red lipstick on the vanity. Fingernail paints, aspirins, cream-of-cow body lotion, hairpins, an enormous brassiere draped over the chair like an unfurled flag. Just wait till I tell Valentine, Hammel. Just you wait, you and fat Elsa. Sitting at the vanity, she wipes the night's dried tear-lines from her eyes, patting the skin smooth with her fingertips; then, with a smile meaning vengeance, she applies her warpaint.

The day's march, christened by the organizers The March for Man, is scheduled to leave Union Square—after a few preliminary speeches—at 9:30 a.m., then gather force and numbers along East 14th Street as far as First Avenue before turning uptown. Bands have been organized to play the usual rally numbers and each of the various political wings is represented by a rostrum of marshals. It is to be an integrated march, communists and socialists and splinter groups all mingled together, a declaration of unity for the cause of man (despite the protests of nitpicking feminists over the title), and the parade is to turn west again at 59th Street, heading toward Central Park for the wrap-up. The route has been carefully planned by the organizers, intending to cut a semicircle through the heart of Manhattan, drawing bystanders, fence-sitters, the terminally bored into the fray, the addition of numbers to the cause contributing to the journalistic, if not entirely sincere, effect. Mounted police will patrol at various checkpoints, keeping the crowd from spilling over into side streets and committing mayhem, but the order has gone out that this is to be a peaceful rally, no stone-throwing or name-calling, simply a demonstration of, of, of.

Valentine, having received a map of the route from a sympathetic communist, has spent hours going over it, walking up and down the arrowed streets from Union Square to Central Park. To stop the flow, he will need a bottleneck, and he has found it, almost by chance, when he turned off First Avenue thinking himself on 28th Street and found himself instead on 29th, where sewer repairs had blocked half the street. Retracing his steps, then crossing the avenue, he came to the front of the wall bordering Bellevue, the city asylum, no way to go but uptown, the planned direction of the march, or downtown, a definite backtrack. The first barricade, phase one, would be thrown up across First Avenue, just above 29th Street, bending the crowd toward the construction area, where phase two would seal off whatever exit might have been offered. The march would have to double back on itself or pass over the Bellevue wall into the asylum grounds. Valentine has no illusions about stopping the march definitively; the mere act of bringing it to a halt will put the Alliance onto page 1, dwarfing any news of crowd size, communist slogans, Wobbly work chants, or the cacophony of a day at the revolution. The trick is to get in and get out before the mounted police arrive but not before the journalists have snapped a few pictures for their front pages.

At eight o'clock, with still no sign of Woudner, Valentine sends his first group off to battle in Lalo's and Eddie's stolen cars. Sylvia, trailing after the others, whispers to him something that he doesn't understand. She repeats it, louder, but still in a whisper: "I have to talk to you."

"Later, Sylvia. Your group is going. Hurry."

"It's important, Val."

"*After* the barricades, Sylvia. *Go!*"

Already the second group is assembling in the living room, some of them pacing, others smoking last-minute cigarettes, waiting for his green light. Hammel, getting angrily out of Lalo's car, whistles for Sylvia to join him. She hesitates, whittling a newly painted fingernail between her teeth, then trips down the short stairway and gets into the car.

For long minutes Valentine stares at his pocketwatch, hoping that Hammel hasn't forgotten the keys to the warehouse they've rented on 29th Street, the repository of garbage, old wood, torn mattresses, and scrap metal. The first group will have less than an hour to load the carts and haul them to the doorway before retreating to their hold positions and awaiting the word from Walter, the scout. Suddenly, Jack is at Valentine's side. "Elsa's gone."

"What do you mean?"

"We just had a headcount. The simple procedure. She's not here."

No time for wondering, no time for second-guessing. One less poet in their midst is no cause for mourning. "We'll do without her," Valentine says. "What was her position?"

"Twenty-ninth Street rooftop. Throwing garbage."

Valentine smiles for the first time that morning.

Jack smiles in return. "I'll tell the others to throw bigger handfuls."

As the second hand sweeps over the twelve, Valentine signals for the second group's departure; then he and Lela climb into Walter's car and head for Union Square. The day is drizzly, threatening rain, a low blank sky seeming to begin just above the bare trees, the pavement slick and littered with Friday night's trash. Wishing Walter good luck, they drop him just below the park and then, although it isn't in the program, Valentine can't resist driving directly to the park to get a look-see. He flicks on his windshield wipers and guesses four to six thousand people in the square, not a very impressive gathering, though more are filtering in from a dozen directions, all heading for the center, where a scaffold has been erected to one side of the fountain, a platform with a large papier-mâché globe hoisted over it, a banner unfurling in the wet breeze: The March for Man. Lined around the platform are men in gray shirts and red caps, blocking the crowd from getting too close to the marshals, and they are holding—can it be?—baseball bats across their shoulders like a pack of haywire Brooklyn Dodgers waiting for the game to begin.

"I know what you're thinking," Lela tells him, "but I'm still coming along."

Love and politics, Valentine is thinking. Poetry and prose. Already he is calculating. Six thousand to start, fifty to a hundred arriving every two minutes, another fifty per ten minutes joining them along the route—there will be at least twelve thousand of them strung along the avenue, a cord that should line up from 29th Street to below 20th. But as he leaves Union Square, turning onto East 14th, he realizes he's miscounted. The march has already begun to string itself forward along the street and the group remaining at Union Square must be the rear guard.

"What is it?" Lela asks.

"They've changed the schedule. Walter will never make it to the barricades ahead of them. He's probably not even to the square by now." Cutting up Park Avenue, he races to 23rd, looking right at every corner, finding the head of the march already as far as 21st Street. Parking the car at the preordained spot on 30th, he tells Lela to stay put but she follows him to the sidewalk and down the street to the corner of First Avenue, where Gregory stands reading a day-old newspaper, keeping an eye out for Walter. Valentine explains the change in plans and Gregory says, "No way, Val. Those carts are only half full by now. We won't have time for the main barricade."

"Give the signal anyway."

"Val, listen. No one, and I mean no one, is in position."

"I said go!"

In the warehouse, only four of the six carts for the first phase have been prepared, and Valentine hurries to help fill the remaining two. He cuts his hand on a sheaf of scrap metal, and a trail of blood follows his arm to the wrist. Sylvia, breaking away from the others, tells him she has to talk to him, he has to listen.

"Help me with this basket!"

Hammel and Valentine lift the basket to the cart, where, from above, Lalo packs it into a corner, old fruit that will tumble to the street, leaving the pavement viscous and unnavigable. Gregory bursts in the side door to announce that the march has reached 27th Street. The sixth cart is only half full but Valentine decides to let it go, calling for everyone to get into place. Olivia, Eleanor, the two winos, and Roger head up the stairs to one roof while Jenny, Sylvia, and half a dozen others climb to another rooftop, the bins of garbage and mattresses already in supply. Lalo and Eddie run to their parked cars, and the remaining men roll the carts onto the street, emerging onto the corner of First and 29th just as Walter, gasping and clutching his sides, arrives at the front door. "They're here."

Glancing upward, Valentine can see Sylvia leaning over the rooftop. She is shouting something to him but he can't hear her above the noise of the approaching marchers. The head of the group is at the intersection of First and 28th, less than a hundred yards away. On Valentine's signal, the men shove the carts toward the center of the street and at that moment the front-most marshals catch wind of what they're about to confront. Two mounted police gallop ahead, clubs raised. The first three carts are tipped forward just as the horsemen arrive and, forgoing Valentine's signal, the women pelt them from above with whatever they can lay their hands on, raining down tomatoes, old shoes, broken furniture, useless radios, mattresses, chunks of wood. Before the remaining carts can be overturned, Lalo and Eddie come screaming from their parking spots, the two hot Packards crashing headlight to headlight, sealing the last gap before the marshals and remaining cavalry can breach it.

As anticipated, the marshals veer left, onto 29th Street, the width of their ranks reduced from twelve to six, and Valentine can barely hear the whistle, Gregory signaling to the second group. A half-dozen carts appear from nowhere and are overturned near the construction ditch. A patrol of police, blocked by the marchers on First Avenue, digs its way to 27th, intending to circle around by way of Second Avenue. Sensing this, Valentine calls to those left on the street to run for it. Lela, off to one side, clings to a warehouse door, her eyes wide, and when Valentine reaches her, she points upward toward the rooftop, shouting, "There, Val! Up there!" His eyes scan the eave and for a second he catches the flash of an outthrust arm. Before he can say the word, the bottle bomb crashes into the street just below the barricade and bursts into flame. As the police approach, another half-dozen fly skyward, falling directly in front of them and forming a wall of flame that licks and spreads to the overturned carts, igniting them.

"Get to the car, Lela."

"Not without you."

"I'll join you later. Go!"

She runs, never to forget her running. Turning once, she sees Valentine enter the warehouse, but she doesn't go after him. She runs.

Leaping over debris, Valentine climbs seven flights of metal stairs to the top, where he is met by Hammel, a bottle bomb in either hand, saying, "I knew it, Val. I knew you'd join us."

"Get out of my way!"

There are a dozen of them, lighting and tossing bottles willy-nilly to the street below. Other than Lalo and Hammel, he has never seen any of them. They are the invisible army he has always feared, his mother's assassins. Sirens are sounding in the distance, and from the rooftop he can see Lela getting into a car with Gregory and Jack and Sylvia, and for a moment his heart stops as they drive away, safe, mingling with the Sunday traffic. Then, swinging round, he gathers up all the bottles within reach and begins to empty them. When Hammel tries to stop him he pushes the man away with one arm and continues pouring with the other. "It's no use," a voice tells him and for a moment he thinks it is his own, that voice he hears daily while he churns out his essays, his poetry, his letters-to-the-editor, waging his paper war and bleeding of ink.

"It's no use, Valentine. The main bomb will detonate any second now."

Still emptying the bottle, he stands and turns and is face to face with Woudner, the glint of his spectacles somehow too bright, shielding his eyes from view.

"*You.*"

"I tried to tell you. The revolution will not be painless. There will be corpses paving the way, perhaps even yours. A bill to settle, no pennies, no fractions . . ."

His fingers on Woudner's throat are as steel around wood, closing slowly finger over finger, while something like a rain, fists, beats him across the head and shoulders. When he comes to, scarce moments later, Woudner is coughing and vomiting on the rooftop and a semicircle of police, rifles poised, moves forward, pinning the anarchists against the near wall. Valentine struggles to his feet, seeing Hammel, Lalo, and the others with their arms upraised, reaching for clouds to drag them elsewhere while below the firetrucks have gone to work, spraying the flames of garbage and gasoline. Woudner stands, retching, and scuttles away from the police, edging his way toward the far wall. "The bomb," he says. "It should have gone off by now."

The police close in, bores trained two to a man on the now-panicked flamethrowers. Woudner, seeking to right himself against the railing, stumbles once, then leans far over, his eyes searching the length of the asylum wall. "Any time now. Any single second." No one but Valentine is watching as Woudner turns, his face ashen, to confront for the last time his long-awaited firing squad. Then he unmistakably leaps (though the police report will say he fell and others will claim he was pushed) and his body, circling once head over heels, lands upon one of the overturned carts, scattering sparks but no flame across the littered sidewalk.

"Which of you is the leader?" one of the policemen is asking. Valentine, his back to a rifle, watches the crowd hurry to encircle Woudner's corpse, all eyes on the smoldering criminal (or martyr: the history will be written ambidextrously).

"I said, which of you is the leader?"

Valentine, turning round, feels their collective gaze, a blinking in his direction.

A police sergeant, eyes bristling, steps forward, taking him by the arm. "You, then. *You* come with *me*."

They are descending the stairway in pairs and just as they reach the ground floor the bomb ignites, tearing a twelve-foot hole in the asylum wall, opening Bellevue to the plain view of the masses. As Valentine is thrust into the paddy wagon, he wonders at Woudner's intentions. Do we go in or do they come out? But already they have pinned him to the floor of the wagon and the rain has begun to fall, clubs, fists, boots, they are on him like a pack of dogs, each of them wanting a piece of him, a bruise, a cracked bone, a souvenir. Valentine, feeling a tooth come loose in the back of his mouth, holds it for a moment like a host on his tongue, a host transforming into a bullet, and then a poison seed, and he swallows it whole.

IN WHICH PAGE STARGAZES

Cheap philosophy, like a twenty-five-watt bulb, burns dull in the night as I sit on the rooftop, stargazing. Jane started it with a snatch of conversation about sitting on bridges and choosing sides. She watches the river flowing toward her while I watch it flowing away. "Come over to my side of the bridge, Page."

"I'm still thinking it over."

"That sound you hear in the background is my tapping foot."

"Don't lose the rhythm. I'm getting there."

And now I'm at the top of her high rise with a choice of looking downward into the machinery of the city or upward into the gears and girders of heaven. There is no moon to fix my gaze and the sky is what the poet Patchen called "a deep throw of stars" but these hold no fascination for me, being neither subject nor object, their light less than .01 watt and not the shiver of a solitary BTU.

I have a gig, or, in photography terms, an assignment. Gabriel has put me in touch with a rich old flake named Weatherstone who has a project embedded in paranoia, just the thing for an invalid Page somewhere in the brackets of war and a Manhattan R & R. Weatherstone wants pictures of the New York sky, though not your cocktail-table anthology of watercolor sunsets, rumbles of cumulus and cirrus, color washes of chemical blue over New Jersey, but analytical frames like Pap smears that will show up under scrutiny some dark truth about the New York skyline. Weatherstone has this theory that some alien aura has covered the city like a great invisible dome. As human and industrial waste rises, the exhaust, carbon, metamorphosed waste is reprocessed by the aura, which converts, or perverts, human spiritual (lighter-than-air) waste into something of a rain that falls perpetually, silently, invisibly, penetrating Manhattan with an ambience, or vapor, of unseemly malice. The steamy neon of 42nd Street; the humid doorways of the East Village; Puerto Rican sweat on the Upper West Side. "All of our evils concentrated into a finite geographical space, unable to escape, to be entirely eliminated through helio-combustion, because of the absolute intensity of this aura. There is no way for our sickness to get through to the cleansing rays of the sun. God, good, the truer spirit. Don't ask me for a name, Mr. Page, because a name, any name, would imply religion where I mean to speak of physics. The sick body reabsorbs its own illness, breathes of it, takes it into its pores. Grows pale and beastly. You've been to the South Bronx? Terminal, utterly terminal. What I need are photographs, proof of this aura, an image of its face. I have to see it for myself."

"Why not hire a scientist?"

"I already have, dozens, and all of them have failed. Something in their straightforward vision, their logic, their equations in chalk, their If Then Else. What I need is an artist, someone with a crooked or, to be kind, *oblique* way of looking at things. A human lens rather than a Cartesian microscope."

"Why me?"

"Your war photographs. The glamour of death in them. I have a copy of your *Hong Kong Folios* and I consider it to be among my prized possessions. It's no wonder you were arrested. . . ."

"I wasn't . . ."

"Trifles. Details. The book was seized, was it not?"

"And the plates destroyed. Negatives burned." He is referring to my first run-in with the law. A minor publication of bad conceptual war art that was seized by someone from upstairs and turned to trash.

"Their fumes," Weatherstone added, "could only have augmented that death cloud over Manhattan. In any case, you have a sharp eye for evil, and of course there's the element of your wound." He gestured to my forehead. "I can even see the shadow of it in this awful lamplight. Do you suffer much? Excellent. I'm certain you're the man for the job."

So to work. I am on Jane's rooftop, twenty-fourth floor of a twenty-three-floor high rise, having taken the express elevator after buzzing Jane to get in the front door. She'd wanted me to come to her place first to say a fast hello to little Hunter but I sidestepped that one by saying maybe later.

It's already half past midnight and I hurry to set up my equipment, the half-dozen cameras on tripods aimed at various angles, each loaded with a different-numbered film, and a six-way shot chronometer that I hold in my hand. I am going all-out tonight, on my own entirely now that Weatherstone has ducked out of the city to escape the aura, taken a Lear jet back to Zug in Switzerland, where the aura seems to weaken but can almost be seen burning over the megabanks of Zurich. Mists of blood money rising from the penumbra. Numberless accounts relying on an oral code, evil's language guarding over the wealth of the cynics in a country of postcard villages, snows, sweets, and that Heidi fright wig. "A loathsome place," Weatherstone has said. "The Zurich Hauptbahnhof is filled with cheeky boys carrying automatic rifles. Forget those Swiss watches and the cuckoo clocks. Look into the alleys and you'll see the Turks squatting in the darkness and passing cigarettes; the garbage collectors and sewer cleaners who maintain this Helvetican hell."

A last tip: "The aura may undulate or respire or something of that nature. It is doubtful that its presence would show up as a straight line on an oscilloscope. Watch for a throbbing, an ebb and flow, any kind of arrhythmic pulse."

What I'm after is a choreographed set of overlays, setting my cameras at crosses and right angles, timing them to frame per 3.5 seconds (f/3.50) or f/2.55, any multiple of half-seconds, so that some of the frames will be isolated but others might be overlaid, the same view from a different, or oblique, angle. Now and then I wonder if maybe this whole gig isn't a bit ridiculous but I'm happy to have a shot at such ultra-expensive equipment. Weatherstone pays, not Page. And last night's proofs turned out more interesting than I'd expected, those photos of blank night space through variously colored filters. The texture of the dark, moonless and unbroken, had been variable and profound, much more than simple snapshots of distance into distance. Captions fail them, as with paintings. The proofs are too liquid, too vague. Far, Cold, Silent, BlueBlackBlue, Ether, Deep. Tonight's overlays may only be more of the same, simple concatenations of Deep Ether, Far Silent, Cold Deep, and no trace of that fine mascara Weatherstone is looking for, the nose or lips or chin of malice. Some of the photos had shown random specks that I couldn't identify as birds, fingerprints, or dust. This morning the first envelope went out to Zug by registered mail. You find it, Weatherstone, I can't.

I listen for helicopters and hear only the traffic of cars. Moving around the rooftop, I adjust and readjust the chronometers, keeping a written log of the time so that Weatherstone will later be able to label the proofs and correlate them—1:12 Cam A, NNW, 86°, f/6.00, etc.—the kind of documentation the old man insists upon. A welcome breeze blows inward from the Hudson, cooling the sweat along my forearms, and I find myself soothed from the constant tilt of looking heavenward, my neck bent to an equal 86°, following the path of my lens, looking if not searching, observing if not seeing. Now and then I pour myself a swallow of Jack Daniel's, telling myself to go easy, and when a few random drops of rain begin to fall I can't help smiling, thinking in Weatherstone terms of my own waste, my mortality, seeping back into my pores, polluting me.

Next, Jane, I will feel my age. Then I might tell you the truth about Hunter. Anyway, who needs this aura when you've got Jack Daniel's?

Elsewhere. Another time, once. Dune Buggy had said he couldn't live forever and I'd told him maybe not even to the end of the year. Walking on a beach of sand, crushed coral, and spent shells, we'd passed that bottle of Jack Daniel's back and forth, neither of us looking out to sea but watching instead the contour of the shore, the uneven line of demarcation between our hothouse garden of Vietnam and La Mer Pacifique. I was avoiding in myself a recognized welling of five-and-dime philosophy, something that often overcame me when I was far from contact, isolated and safe. Turning it all into symbolism, the killing and burning, was a very cheap trick, better left to the historians and those long-haired kids back at the world. That had become Dune Buggy's problem, too much thinking about it, too much looking for *the words to say it*. By this time he'd been in for about six months but already was saying things like "Let's win this one for Dow Chemical and Chase Manhattan." Or "The web is growing wider and the flies are dying one next to another. Who's the spider, Wide Eyes? Who's gonna be having my soul for breakfast?" Sartre in jungle fatigues, handing me a bottle.

Snap and whir. I took three shots of him standing on the beach in khaki shorts and sunburn, a raised hand shading his eyes from the setting sun as he looked inland over my shoulder. "So now what?" I'm telling him it's time to go to the cathouse and get wasted. The Jack Daniel's was empty and we were both still stone-cold sober.

"Don't think so much about it, Dune Buggy. Get yourself stoned or laid or something. Or do like I do."

What is it I do?

Snap and whir. A fifteen-year-old did these poses for me, just for me, she said, her legs raised high, catch this act, Joe, and this one. She pulled down the lampshade with her big toe and the final print had been a blur of light becoming darkness, flashy stuff but I couldn't sell it. Lying on a sofa embroidered in blue nylon, dragons eating their own tails, she'd offered anything grotesque, *anything* Joe Blow wanted. Snap. Whir. This was the night we met Chulin, a real amateur of a whore, and argued over which of us would beat up her pimp. I was in favor of blackjacking him and skipping out on the sly, but Dune Buggy wanted to take him face to face like a hero. Clicka shicka. Once we were in a quiet hotel I got busy with homelier stuff, but there is still a print of Chulin noticing her nakedness, the thin arms and tiny breasts, and the frame is hot with her shame. What I didn't photograph is Dune Buggy covering her with his shirt or myself falling into her arms and saying I'm sorry at least a dozen times and the two of us making love to her without any money intervening all the way to the next morning and then some.

The Western rain is falling on my rooftop and my lenses are getting droplets on their surfaces, so I hurry around gathering things up, film boxes, tripods, filters, and when I'm in the hallway shaking the rain from my sleeves I look up and find Jane standing there as though I were awaited.

"So how's it going?"

"Going?"

"Stop repeating after me. Your work."

"God knows."

"What are you taking pictures of?"

"Heaven."

"Really? See any angels?"

I have a ready-made answer. Yuri Gagarin, the first man ever to orbit the earth, was later asked what he'd seen. "No angels," he'd said. "And no God."

She wants to know if I'm coming downstairs. "Hunter's asleep now. He wouldn't see you seeing him."

I tell her I have business but it doesn't wash.

"And don't tell me about *your* lost father, Page. Not another word of it until you've at least *looked* at this baby. He's got your name and sometimes I swear he has your eyes, too. Come and look. No one is saying you have to stay."

I'm not one of those guys who can carry his office on his back. There are half a dozen tripods, eight cameras, film and lens boxes, the clipboard. Jane helps me load it all into the elevator; then we ride it together to the twelfth floor. Jane steps out but holds her hand over the electric eye to keep the doors from closing.

"You know it's futile, Page. That's why you picked this rooftop. So you could stand up there like his guardian angel while he sleeps."

"I need a clean shirt," I tell her. "I haven't shaved in two days."

"I'll do your laundry. And there's a razor in my bathroom."

I realize that I'm not afraid of Hunter or of Jane. One is a harmless infant and the other a woman who loves me. I've had it worse. What terrifies me is being home. I haven't been here for years and am not convinced I can stop the pacing just like that. If I walk in I'll walk out again and then someone'll get hurt. More cheap philosophy: You can't take back what you haven't given. More still: Don't ask me and you won't have to hear me say no.

"If you don't come soon, he's going to think I made you up."

She has her point of view and it isn't all that oblique, come to think of it. I feel myself stepping out of my shoes but I'm only stepping out of the elevator and following her down the hall, the elevator on hold.

"Are there vandals?" I want to know, thinking of all those cameras left to themselves.

Jane says no, the place is safe. I follow her through the door of her apartment and we cross the dark living room hand in hand, to the hallway, a quick right; then she is nudging open a blue door. A nightlight, Mickey Mouse, glows in the far corner, and through the bars of a crib I can see a cotton bundle. Him, he. Seeing him there, I feel like a lie dressed up for confession. Jane doesn't know the half of it about me and Dune Buggy and Chulin and maybe I don't either. We're standing together, hands laced, looking down into the crib at this sleeping baby. Then Jane says, in a whisper, "Hunter, wake up. Daddy's home."

Through the first ten or eleven years of my life, various bogeymen showed up at Armand's door to lay claim to me, erroneously assuming, no doubt, that I'd inherited the Lela Maar estate. "I knew her in New York early in 1944. She wanted a fix but I held out on her. We went to a hotel and stayed the night and when she was through with her sweating, it happened, the paternity. She called herself Vera but I knew it was her."

"We met in London in a West End pub. I was drinking Guinness but she asked for a martini. No one knew how to make one so she drank gin straight up. Said her name was Mercy, and I didn't know until later who she was. A singer, I mean. When I held her in my arms she was like a dying bird, so thin and all."

"I followed her from New York to Toronto and then to London. My fidelity moved her and we took a flat in Chelsea for a month. She never sang, not once. At night she'd sit quietly on the bed and write letters that she never sent. When she knew she was pregnant, she left me. When I read the news I put two and two together and here I am."

Armand checked the stories and none held water. He must have spent a small fortune on private detectives and I never thanked him, because I didn't see the point of it. But later I did some looking of my own, following up on Armand's work, circling names in biographies and knocking on doors for information. Half of her world was already dead, the other half suffering from that myth-induced amnesia. One old black piano player said my father could have been anyone but him. "Far's I know, she was a virgin to me and me alone. You're hangin on a prayer, son. Take a deep breath and let it go."

So she slept around. So did Chulin and here's Hunter to fret over the mystery of that for just about a lifetime.

Jane wants to know if I'll stay the night. "At least what's left of it?" It is half past three. Without a reason to say no, I retrieve my cameras from the elevator and store everything in the kitchen. Jane is already in her bedroom pulling down the bedsheet and I go to the door to tell her I don't think it's a very good idea.

"Listen, Page, it's been months. I've been faithful and just now I'm a little bit in heat, if you get the picture."

"It's the bed, Jane. I'm not up to a bed."

"Where, then?"

I scout around the living room for a suitable patch of floor and find what I'm looking for in a corner behind the couch. It is dark but I can still see her undressing and her body seems larger to me in that darkness, a towering presence. Coming near to me, she is reduced to what I know, a slim heat moving up and around me. Kissing me once, she tells me to apologize.

"For what?"

"Anything. I want to hear you say you're sorry."

"I'm sorry."

"You're forgiven."

It's penance, then, and not entirely love. When I am slow to excite, she moves down on me until my cock rises like a tree into the sky of her mouth but she stops me, wanting me inside of her. It doesn't last long, a lock and a release and a shivering, and when it is over she is up and around, searching for cigarettes, wine, an ashtray, pretending satisfaction. She tosses me a pillow but I hand it back. "The floor's fine."

We smoke without talking and then I fall asleep and awaken to the sound of a baby crying. Jane nudges me. "You go, Page."

"What does he want?"

"Milk or love. Give him what you've got."

I am halfway across the living room when I feel my nakedness and I am inspired by it, somehow, to be walking without clothes in the day's first light. How Hunter will see me home from the wars, all the scars showing; flesh and blood. At first glance at him, I see what Jane means. He has those Occidental eyes, round as dimes, and they grow larger as I hover over him. When I lift him, he is heavier than I expect, not the weightlessness of rumor, and I can feel his breath on my ear, a delicate vapor of almost words. Within seconds he is asleep and I lay him back down, face first, to his pillow, cover him with a thin blanket, and walk away.

"So?" Jane wants to know.

"So he's sleeping."

"Your eyes are wet."

"Like hell they are."

She kisses my lids and then settles back to the floor. "It's early," she says. "You can abuse me for another hour before I have to go to work."

We begin but before long the phone is ringing and Jane hurries to answer it before the ringing wakens Hunter. "He's not here," I hear her saying. "I haven't heard from him." A pause. "I still have your number, but what's this all about?" Then she drops the receiver and turns to me. "He hung up."

"Who?"

"The army. They know you're in New York."

"Then we're even."

"Why don't you just call them and get it over with?"

"We have things to say to each other. They want me to go to hell and I say I've made reservations. It's a minor matter of scheduling, is all. I haven't yet seen a body bag with my name on it."

"You're being vague, Page. What have you done?"

I admit that I don't really know. "Maybe I've mucked up their history. That war over there, you remember. I've seen things that they say never happened. It's their word against mine."

"Call them up. Tell them you're retired now and that it's over."

I tell her I'm not sure that's the truth of it.

"You're not thinking of going back!"

"I doubt it, but I've doubted things before and then they've happened to me. Life in the intransitive, that's me. I never planned on this career. I didn't plan on you and I didn't plan on Hunter."

"But you took those pictures."

"To kill time, Jane. That's all it's ever been."

The trouble with crawling through a sleepless night into dawn is that the coming light makes you say things aloud that you might otherwise not even say to yourself. It should have been enough to come and see Hunter, but it wasn't. I had to make fast love to Jane to keep the peace and now she wants words, phrases like quarters for her personal jukebox. But she's a woman and maybe all she really wants is not to be so lonely. I feel I should be more lively company but it seems that putting a ring on her finger and calling her my old lady would be a screaming injustice to both of us. Page, you flop. "Why don't you ever slap me?" I ask her.

But she's already moved away from me a perceptible foot and is hugging her arms round her breasts, pushing them upward, making that sweet V. "Someone else has been calling," she says. "He's called three times this week. He says he's your father."

I've seen this movie and am not amused. "He's too late. I'm not looking anymore."

"He told me his story, Page. I think you should listen."

I tell her otherwise. "I've heard all these stories already, written and oral. Years and years ago. We looked hard for him, first Armand and then me. It's thirty years ago, why would he show up now?"

"You're asking me?"

"There's a whole raft of fathers anyway. It's a goddamn country club. One father killed himself just after the war. He took a bottle of sleeping pills and fell asleep on top of a bridge. His body fell and was washed ashore on Ellis Island. That's Harry Lord. Another father died in a bomb test in 1956. He went looking for it and there isn't a trace left of him. That's Valentine. The others are these shadowy figures, names on lists, suspects. Some man in England . . ."

"He said he knew her there."

"He's lying through his teeth."

"He says he has proof."

"Look, just because you answer the phone doesn't mean you have to listen. Knock on wood a little and you'll find it's just pressboard. Made up, right? Conjured."

"He wants very much to see you."

In Southeast Asia, they build houses out of bamboo and palm, easy-to-assemble kits of beam and crossbar, because they know the wind is going to blow and there isn't anything to be done about it. That wind comes tearing in from heaven and the house will fold up like an envelope and have to be reassembled. Get those bars up and gather grass for the rainy season. No thought of stone and mortar or a permanence beyond the next monsoon. That wind will come back anyway, so why fight it? Someone's always shrugging and saying singsong *c'est la vie,* man. Next time the house comes falling down on your upraised head, you just whistle howdy and then get up and build another. That's what Jane's after now. To see me shrug and smile and say, Why not, why in hell not give this man a call? Where you been? I've been expecting you.

When Armand and Elaine died in that car wreck I had to go down to the morgue to look at them. Some guy in a white jacket said, Is this your father?, and I said he was. Bamboo and palm fronds were all over the place, a real mess. I followed up on Armand's search and put more of the pieces together, looking for the next father just up the road. And every damn time there came that wind stinking of botched history to blow the whole thing down again. After a while I got the picture and voted with my feet. I knew which way the wind blew and I headed the other way.

LELA MAAR SINGS HARRY LORD

"FROM HERE TO TUESDAY"
(4:04)

1939

She is not a star, a raging luminosity in the farflung firmament, but a legend still underground, a shadow on the margin of musical history.

Lela reads this in the *Herald Tribune,* the writer alluding to her. She asks Harry what it means and he only says it means she's the greatest.

"That's not what it says."

Not a star, but a legend, Lela Maar . . .

There seems to be a difference.

"Something about how you'll last instead of burning out. The years and all."

Denied stardom, she settles for the notoriety of being an original. . . . She reads the article twice, a third time, the living legend learning what she has become. Her relentlessness and her yearning, all of her engagements come to this. "Harry, I'm not sure I *want* to be a legend."

Later, in bed, she decides the writer got it wrong. These little girls mournfully gazing into mirrors do not want to see Lela looking back at them, lips parted, ready to sing. *That's* a legend, mister; me, I just sing and am the idol of no one. A nightclub singer in Jersey threw herself out of a twenty-story window for love and in the month that followed there were a dozen imitation suicides, failed songstresses doing as she did, and some of them even got into the papers for it. But dying isn't in Lela's contract; singing is. She decides she'll become a legend later in life.

For the moment, I'm still flesh and blood.

As so often happens in the night, far from the music, listening to the occasional passing taxi five floors below, all she can hear above the electric tides of the city is a deadly whisper saying it won't last forever it won't last can't . . . making her get up and reach for Harry's hand, awakening him, telling him they have to work, the song isn't right.

Harry, by now almost acclimated to Lela, her Olympic highs and her subterranean lows, sits up and runs a hand through his hair. "The song. Mmn. This morning you loved it."

"But now it's night, Harry. Get dressed."

This is how they work together: 3:00 a.m. at the piano, Harry wearing only his pants, Lela in bra and half-slip sipping whisky to calm a scratchy throat. A single lamp lit over the keyboard so Harry can see his hands and the score in front of him.

Play it through, Harry. To the end, and I'll catch you.

You're shaking, Lela.

The cold, the heat. I've got a fever.

She has to pause here and there where Harry's left the bars blank, to be filled in with Skate's saxophone; his wind blows against the stone of Harry's piano. They always call in Skate when the song is ready, don't even have to tell him much about what they want, the man seems to *know*, trill, slur, and spiral like that serpent, some call it applied evil and others call it the Gift. Lela stops Harry in mid-roll to scratch out a line of lyrics, rewriting what once was his into her own, their time-tested method.

You listen for the sweethearts, Harry, and I'll put the devils in their beds.

Again, again, again. Time smears light across the curtain. Harry shanks a chord, fatigue setting in like a drug. Lela blows him a kiss. Again, we'll do it again.

From here to Tuesday / With time on my hands / Got this dying feeling / No one understands

The man says she's a legend but not a star. Ella Fitzgerald sells a hundred thousand records, Lela much less than half that. But she inspires something rabid in the shadier zones of the music world. A Boston critic holds his fingers to his nose but for every one of him there is someone like the young cripple in Detroit who sweeps his daddy's bar every morning, spending his pay a nickel at a time to play over and over again "Slow Train Don't Come" and wondering why Lela don't sing the blues more often. Or the same sad-looking lady every night at the same club, same table, same faded green dress, nursing a single highball through three long hours, and after every song requesting "Long Fall . . . ," and even after Lela's done it and the applause and the table-thumping have died down and the bassist is already revving up for the next number, the lady half rises from her chair, eyes afire, saying, "Sing it, sing it again."

This is where the song ends but Lela's still singing. This is where it ends but it isn't ended. She is still singing and the song is at its end and she is singing.

"From Here to Tuesday" will be their first record under a new label. Harry has passed up a renewal offer from Black Dot to go over to John Rose Ltd., an English company with a jazz label called Sentiment. White Star has too many musicians under contract and imposes them on the recordings. Lela, swamped in strings and bound by clarinets, has too often sounded like some big-band dolly. The only thing that had really worked was "When You, How You, Do You," one of the fastest numbers Harry ever wrote, even if it was Lela who decided on the tempo. Small-minded critics carped about the chord changes and the almost complete disregard for the rules of key progression; while Harry'd fretted, Lela'd dug. Spontaneous composition hadn't yet set its teeth to the task but Lela, in nightclubs, had gotten into the habit of pulling her head away from the microphone, and the ululations of her voice had added yet another signature to her style.

From here to Tuesday / With nothin to do / Sit by the rainin window / Forgetting you

Harry had written "Slow Train Don't Come" just after the wedding in Baltimore and Lela had taken six kinds of heat from her musical black sisters because of the way she'd sung it, her speech slurred and jazzed and Negroid. They'd thought she'd been funning them, mocking them, and all she'd had to say was, That's the way it had to be sung, so go get wet.

Harry was conception and Lela adaptation. He said a church wedding and she said, We'll live in sin. So he'd changed tactics, bringing out a suitcase full of tax forms, PR notes, hotel receipts, man & wife being less expensive than man & woman, all these paper arguments, and she'd given in, loving him anyway, in need of him, and certain—especially just before the lights went down, her heart a sparrow's panicked beat—that without him, his piano, and his melodies, she would spin from the earth into blank space,. legend's oblivion. She'd said yes and she'd also said, No babies, not just now, so they'd been married in privacy, in Baltimore, paying a witness ten dollars to get the news to a radio station, then had waited in driving rain for the last night train to Penn Station. Somewhere in that rain was the song. Harry and the weather wrote it on paper while Lela slept.

Near dawn, Harry puts the last touches to "From Here to Tuesday." Lela's bottle is empty and her throat is shot with needles, her fever worsened but adding a low urgency to her singing, a breathlessness that gives the song all the more gravity. Tragic stuff, this jazz of Harry Lord, the kind of music that sends sentimental types to the balcony and wiseguys to the bar for another double, straight up. Lela says they better think about recording it, "And soon, before I get over this blessed cold," so Harry calls the studio and tells them they're coming while Lela checks out the kitchen cupboard for another bottle of throat lotion.

She feels herself in love, a lover. If Harry's wife, she is also Harry's spoiled bride, Harry's changeling, Harry's hell and honey and fame. Harry is to her an inspired keyboard, his music fragile but menacing, bordering on the terrible (one note either way on the scale could tip some awful balance). Same thing for the marriage. Lela, see, has this itch, can't quite call it desire since it's not quite as *fine* as that; can't locate it between her legs either, though that may be where she scratches from time to time, her sin of other men, alternatives, though to her they are scents, clues, fragments of some whole presence, no, not steppingstones, there being no river to cross anymore. These men are just there, saying *beautiful*, saying *thorny*, saying it into her ear and her skirt, wanting to rub up against her and her success, wanting to play themselves somewhere within her as if in some way to go along with her, beyond her spread legs and into her yawning legend.

There is, then, no marriage. Not really. There is only the musical tribe. Men and women crawl in and out of love tents in the night, a fire lazily burning, sending smoke like whispered lies of love upward, and there is always some ambitious debutante around to stir the embers. You and me, babe. We're going places, just you watch.

Harry, I'm off to the nightclub.

Catch you later, babe.

Consider, then, these jazz people in their hotel rooms during four-night stands on the road, haven't seen a dawn in weeks, noon is the first hour of every day and it is spied through the lens of a hangover, the blues, and a thirst that has nothing to do with water or wine. Consider the tribe at 4:00 a.m., around that time when the drummer gets up from the couch with some faceless girl, a hanger-on, tipping over a dry bottle (nothing left to spill), and heads down the hall to his numbered room, wisps of marijuana and tobacco smoke haloing the two of them. Consider this. Harry sleeps the sleep of composers and saints on the third floor while Lela, two flights up, says to Skate that he better be more careful this time, last time she was sore for a week, I'm a woman, not a mattress, be more gentle.

From here to Tuesday / Nothing will last / I'll walk on heartbreak / Like broken glass

The recording session goes off like silk, Harry's piano right on the money with rippled and resolute runs that line in spades the remoteness of Lela's stripped-naked voice, Skate barely awake and his horn laconic and *just so.* As they leave the studio, some engineer says it's a hit and Harry only smiles while the legend, wrapping her arms round herself and squeezing forth a magnificent set of lungs, says, I'm beat, dead, won't someone take me home?

Josephus Cait, formerly of Selma, Alabama, and the unforgiving grandson of a slave woman, was once the alto sax in the Band of Black Gabriel. Those are his sugary licks you hear weaving behind Alvin Little's unforgettable trumpet solos. The early recordings, the ones everybody says they had a copy of and never should have lent away. It was Alvin Little, mistaking the cadence of his name, who first called him Skate. The trumpet artist may have had a perfect embouchure, strengthened by constant spitting of rice, chick peas, and kernels of hard corn, but his hearing was always vaguely askew. Witness his "Summertime Solos" of 1929, which are filled with unintentional dissonance, his malady being mistaken for innovational genius.

Early in his career, Skate had what is known as a wet reed, too much spit leaving him with a tendency to slur one quarter-note over another. Chewing lemons helped but only after a few years of hard drinking and several hundred packs of Lucky Strikes was he able to overcome his salivation. He played clean then. That's what Alvin Little asked for.

When Skate started testing heroin, that old-time favorite of jazz musicians, Alvin blew his top. "That trash won't get you nowhere but unemployed. Get you-self straight." Playing behind Alvin was still a breeze but he began to have this problem with the tempo: he couldn't pick it up and sustain it anymore. Nor was his wind ever the same. Whole notes were unintentionally dotted or tremoloed. One night when Skate was off in the ozone, Alvin said to him, "Josephus, man. Your reed is getting thin. You know what I'm sayin?" Skate knew. In 1931 he was replaced by Bobby Sing, the black Chinese, and so switched to tenor sax, figuring wind might not be all of it and the tenor sax took less hard lung than the alto.

Word got around and Skate's news was old news. Eight years of that, right up until Lela, who has a weakness for that occasional orphan note of his, a singular trailing something he lays at the end of every run; his dying fall. He hooks up with Harry and Lela on her insistence, though he doesn't see much future in strutting and swaying with whitey in no New York music-hall universe. And he can never quite get past the emptiness of the years after Alvin Little banished him from the big time. He'd become a journeyman, a musical nomad, tagging along with unknown bands for low-paying strings of gigs in bars between nowhere and not much of where. Nowadays, a reedy hundred and twenty pounds of failure, he relies on his sandy tongue and his killing good looks. Skate is a ladies' man and his music gets him by. He has this notion, not quite a philosophy, that he is on earth to play women as well as saxophones and the music of one is not so unlike the music of the other. He can make that baby trill, whistle, wheeze, or wail; dig it, he once even wrote it down in notes, skipping over those mattress percussion sounds, remembering afterward all the sounds of *her*. On his sax he can play it almost as it was, only the pitch eludes him. We'll have to work on that, baby.

Like how?

Like you come too loud.

You breakin my heart.

He hears her and plays some heartbreak on his sax, sitting there naked on the edge of the bed, cry cry cry, and then Lela, calling him at dawn, says he should get his ass to the studio, time to cut a record. Lela may be white but that's better than no color at all. He pulls on his pants, not enough time for a wake-up shot, feels a chill in his joints and something like a mosquito in his inner ear. Packs a nickel bag and his kit, spoon and candle and needle, into his jacket.

Where you headed, Skate?

Got a gig. Keep it warm.

Skate chips. Which is to say he has avoided the mainline for all of his nine years in the land of H. When he starts to sweat, he goes dry, starving his blood and living hellish weekends from Friday to Monday, crying in his dirty bed, dreaming junk dreams, and spitting into a reed of pain. All the hurt of a body saved up through weeks of little shots, happy doses, just enough for a nod or two and some uneasy slumber. He's seen all the hard guys up in Harlem scratching away at needlemarks, thinking junk is medicine for no talent, nodding out over their own keyboards, all out a finger pop, bop bop, swing. So Skate chips, little tastes at a time, or else he can't play, and if he can't play no amount of white shit is going to get him safely from dusk to dawn and back again.

Sitting in a taxi, shivering for no good reason, he knows he's overdue for a cleanup. The horse is moving too fast, too fast, picking up to a full gallop, and he can't sleep so good, can't hold his food down, even last night with Hattie he could hardly get it up at all till she jazzed him with her hands and mouth and all. Time to slip the saddle, sit still on some dry ground, catch his breath, get his eyes pried open.

At the studio they're all waiting for him, ready to go, the back-line musicians tuned and set, Harry sitting moody as ever at the ivories, working out some high run with his right hand, Lela looking especially white getting up from a chair with a flask in one hand and a lyric sheet in the other to blow him a kiss. Somebody's saying, Let's roll, and Skate gets behind a mike and clips his sax to a necklace, swaying a little, trying to keep his knees together, can't play sitting down, gotta stand up. Sweat runs down his lip to his tongue and he licks it away while Harry starts the number with a left-hand riff until the back line picks him up and Skate, getting a nod from the Lord, lifts the reed to his tongue, leans the horn against his hip, listens for the first wail from Lela, and breathes it back upon her.

Lighting a match, she holds it between thumb and forefinger, breathing in the sulphur. The flame heads downward toward her polished nails, burning too quickly somehow, and though she trembles it does not go out, but burns her. The hurt. That night she sings badly, as she knew she would, and in bed Harry seems to be holding a grudge. He sleeps across the water, his back impenetrable.

*

Do it again.

That's the best I can do, Harry.

I've heard better. Bring it up higher.

Harry, I'm beat.

Again, Lela. With a vengeance.

Skate saying: Leave her be, man. Can't you see she's having one of her times?

Mid-September and the glory is getting strewn around over "From Here to Tuesday." The first press of twenty thousand copies is sold out, and Lela steps into a taxi, giving the driver an address on the Lower East Side. Taking a mirror from her purse, a gift from Harry shaped into a pentagon, an almost star, she inventories eyes, nose, lips, smoothing her lipstick with a forefinger, forming a kiss.

He is waiting for her, even opens the front door of the brownstone before she can ring the bell. The years in prison have scarcely changed him, or her memory of him is that imperfect; no snapshots lying around to freeze and ruin time in two black-and-white dimensions. He has the same manner of standing very erect, his head tilted slightly backward, shoulders back. Only his eyes are altered, still burning with something unnamable, but that something has gone from blue to black, a stare where once was a gazing. Over the phone he'd asked her how she'd known he was out.

"I read it in the paper." A two-inch item without headline, buried under the staggering news from Europe, the lightning war.

"Do you remember the address?"

"I'm on my way."

After the bombing, his trial had been swift, the verdict harsh: twelve years in Attica, though he'd been released after only nine. Hammel, Lalo, and the others had done less than a year, and now Hammel is said to own a corner grocery in Queens while Lalo is invisible but presumed to be with the radical anarchists. Sylvia, Walter, Eleanor, Eddie, Elsa:

all vanished, departed into the wings of obscurity, or simple event, no lines left in the script for them, no stage directions.

Valentine invites Lela inside and they sit in what was once the massive dining room and meeting hall, the table now cleared of papers, only a vase of half-dead flowers in the center, into which Valentine pours fresh water.

"Carelessness," he says to Lela, who sits nervously before him, folding and unfolding her hands, "has always cost me dearly. I bought these flowers yesterday and only just now, waiting for you to come, I realized that I'd put them into a dry vase."

The room has that saddening smell of neglect, the windows closed for months, swooning oxygen, stale memories, whatever might once have been vibrant and eager having gone to seed, perhaps leaving a patina atop the wide mahogany table, a yellow something seeping into the flowery wallpaper, killing even those print roses. The sunlight that falls inward through the curtains is like the sunlight in a museum, radiating nothing but the millions of particles of dust, sunlight that falls to the floor and lies there unmoving, not a shadow stirring.

They sit quietly for a time, both of them visitors here, while Lela sips tea and Valentine watches her, pretending to smile. Here we are, you and I. Whatever he is feeling, he isn't about to describe to her. Let her ask.

When she mentions Jenny he remembers to tell her that Jenny is dead. "In her sleep, three years ago. That's why the house is so unused." The words seem to hurt him, taking his breath away. But he rallies, saying that he runs into Jack every now and then. "He's still at it, still a believer. We have to be so careful, it's almost funny. I'm still considered a criminal." Standing, he approaches the window and looks out. "I have a shadow now," he says, referring to the agent across the street. "He's wasting his time. There was no Alliance for me to come home to. While I was in prison, no one called or wrote. Those who were pacifists blamed me for the bombing. Some of them even looked upon Woudner as something of a martyr. He had the good grace to die like Joan of Arc, even if the pyre was made up mostly of garbage."

She asks him about his plans.

"Nothing's really certain. I can live here for a while, but the house won't be mine for long. Meantime I walk around the city and enjoy my freedom. And I'm writing a book."

This is news to her, the first sign of his survival. "What about?"

He doesn't know. "I only know how to write. It's all I can do. When I've finished enough pages, there will be a book. Something to read."

"A book of history?"

"No," he says, the faintest smile on his lips. "A book of words."

She has finished her tea and they have nothing more to say. They rise and go into the bedroom, Valentine turning back the bedsheet, and he undresses her swiftly, tearing at the buttons on her dress. "In prison, I had a man," he tells her. "It was loveless but we always itched for each other. Closing our eyes and imagining a woman." When she is naked he enters her and she submits to him, moving with him just enough to abet his coming, which is brief and sudden and seems to pain him. When she thinks he is going to weep, she weeps herself, while his eyes remain dry and distant. Lifting himself from her body, he shields himself from the daylight, pulling the sheet to his waist.

"You haven't forgiven me for running off."

For the first time he truly touches her. Fucking doesn't count. His face in the arc of her neck, he says no, he forgave her from the beginning. It is himself he has never forgiven. "I should have gone with you." There had been enough room in his prison cell for an autobiography of regret, confession, constellations of grief, and though he hadn't bothered to X the days off the calendar, he had been aware of the emptying grains from one pyramid to another, the hourglass of his life more than a decade wasted. "That bomb undid everything, but most especially the illusion that I was living for a cause. It was my mother's legacy, my whole past. While other kids were reading *Robinson Crusoe,* I was going through back issues of *Mother Earth.* Maybe that's why I sometimes felt so at home in prison, among other criminals, killers, rapists, thieves, amateur revolutionaries like me. Prison is a place for *failures* and, believe me, that place had a stink of smoke to it; not the smoke of a fire but of something smoldering and full of ashes. I wanted to work in the library but so did everyone else, the place was so full of deep thinkers and third-rate Lenins and Bakunins, everybody writing memoirs or blueprints for a better world. The first thing to be done, of course, was to empty the prisons. There was even an underground newspaper they passed from hand to hand around the cells, and I've never read such trash in my life. I ended up working in the carpentry shop. They used to give us old newspaper to cover the floor with. One afternoon I was gathering up the newspaper from the floor and I recognized your photo through the sawdust. That's how I read about your marriage."

His hands are no longer as soft as cushions but are broken now, and polished from work; cuts healed to scars, even a sliver of pine still resting within a wedge of callus on the heel of his right hand. Naked, he is trimmer and more muscular, the animal of him more exercised, the poet in him sanded down to bone. Even in bed with her he has a force that defies repose, a tautness that she doesn't remember from their past. She senses that whatever in him is broken will mend; whatever is wounded will heal. This time when he reaches for her she answers with caresses of her own, circling his back with her hands and grasping. He presses his erection against her thigh, the muscles of his ass clenching and unclenching, and then she spreads her legs wide as he hovers over her and descends.

"With that man," he says. "In prison. I closed my eyes but I never thought of you. If I did, I would panic." Her tongue moves over his, muting him, and she turns their easy rhythm into a frenzy, wanting him like that, hurrying him and tracing his back with her nails, hurting him back the good hurt. They fuck the afternoon to its end, till the shadows reach across the bed and engulf them; then at last he rolls away from her, just can't anymore, just can't.

Later, he tells her what his life would be without her and she answers what hers has been without him. He wants to marry her now, believing more in the gesture than the ritual, but she refuses him. She says that someone will always be waiting for her and she will always be hurrying to meet him. With Harry, Valentine; with Valentine, anyone.

"No one's mother but everyone's wife?"

Taking his hands in her own, Lela nods. "That's the way I sing my song."

Leaving the bed, she dresses swiftly, wanting to be either naked or clothed, one thing or another, lover or stranger, here or not here. Harry will be waiting for her, in his chair in the dark, smoking a cigarette and brooding. She will tell him she had no idea of the time. Time is something she has never mastered, the measurement of its passing. Valentine remains in the bed, watching her.

Bending her head to the mirror, she gazes into her own eyes, then turns and asks Valentine what he will do. "Now. This evening. Once I've gone."

He will be walking Manhattan, up and down Broadway, befriending drunks, criminals. He will dine at the mission and be forced to listen to a sermon before breaking bread. He will read a book and add words to his own.

She says it sounds lonely.

He says he has never felt lonely in his life.

As she leaves the brownstone, Valentine's shadow, in suit and tie, nods in her direction, acknowledgment if not consent. He writes her name on a pad of paper, then turns his back to her. When she returns the next day there is a different shadow across the street, his brim pulled low across his eyes, and when she smiles to him he does not smile in return.

For reasons known only to God, Lela always makes love to Harry on trains. Lela Maar sings Harry Lord from Boston to Buffalo, Buffalo to Pittsburgh, Pittsburgh to Indianapolis. Live wires turn out to see the show, shouting out their favorites until 2:00 a.m., Lela giving them what she's got and making no pretense to have more, but when she boards the train she feels that heat in her blood, her piano man transformed, no longer doubting himself, his soul, his seed. It is a minor joke among the other members of the band, all that noise coming from Lord's sleeper in the night, Hattie saying, "Lela, wuzzat *you* I heard singing all night?" though Skate never says much about it. Skate's too cool to acknowledge that other men don't necessarily sleep alone.

This road trip is their longest yet, fourteen cities over three months, but the act is all the rage, the legend notwithstanding, and only in Louisville do they find themselves booed, a cabal of rich spades having shown up to tell the white bitch to quit singing so black, Lela answering from the floor that black folks haven't got a corner on heartbreak. The night ends in broken chairs and collapsed tables, shattered glasses, and spilled whisky leaving fumes of something tragic in the ruin of the nightclub. They hit the road a few days earlier than planned, heading straight for Baton Rouge, the last Southern stop, a place where they'd all hated Billie Holiday but blame Lela for not being her.

Listless hotel hours. Card games and radio shows, checking out the spring of the mattress, the manifold cracks in the ceiling, the pattern of hothouse orchids on the peeling wallpaper, smells of ghosts and anyone who'd come before to sleep or cry or fuck within those walls. When Harry falls asleep, Lela goes wandering, her night never ending that easily, and finds herself before Hattie's door. She knocks and hears a voice asking who.

"Lela."

"It's open."

Skate is there, taping Hattie's arm above the elbow while she's making a fist. A candle is lit and next to it is a bent spoon. The malevolence in Hattie's eyes is as pure as the night. "Have a taste, Missie Maar?"

"No. No, I don't think so."

Skate says, "No skin off me if you don't."

"She'll be back," Hattie says just as Skate slides the needle inward. "She's got the rage."

Everything Hattie says means two things. Lela closes the door behind her and stands stupid and alone in the empty hallway. The other rooms are vacant, Sam and Blake and Slow Curt having gone off to the movies. Sunday night in Baton Rouge and the rain should be coming down any time now. Nothing to do but go home to Harry, awaken him, and make love to him. She does.

When they hit Kansas City, she breaks away from the band and crosses the river to where she came from, the Kansas side, taking a cab to a house on Duquesne Avenue where she spends a long, long time on the sidewalk just looking at what used to be home. A wide front door, sagging porch, paint peeling around the eaves where there used to be vast numbers of spiders and tiny ants marching in long single file from earth to rooftop. Nothing is changed but the lawn, which is now burned out and overcome with dandelions. Here was her anonymity, this box of wood in this field of weeds. No words, no letters, no postcards, no phone calls, long years of no one there to write to but her father. Her mother died when Vera was seven in a car accident with her lover (heading home from the only hotel nearby), her only sister long since married and moved to Arizona with a real-estate loud-mouth husband. Journalists, digging for Lela's past, have come up with nothing, no panties to sniff and to air in public. In interviews, she says only that she's always been there, where've you been, you?

Her father must be listening to the radio, the "Seagram's Hour," maybe Bing Crosby singing, or even the fights broadcast from the Garden. I sang at the Garden, old man, were you listening or was it one of those nights when the bottle was too short, too light, too too, for home? She would go in except that her father is not to be seen, no sign of him anyway in years and years, all she remembers is a man burned black with grief after her mother's death, drinking too much and going whole week-ends without getting dressed, dragging around Sundays in that old green bathrobe, rummaging in the kitchen for a bottle of something bootlegged or polishing any of the artifacts of the shrine to his dead wife, her pictures and her jewelry on the mantel. The dead mother more alive than the living father. And, oh shit, now the rain is really falling and there are no taxis around here so she has to walk almost a mile to a grocer's, where she calls Harry. He arrives within an hour, rain on his sleeve and that same sorrow in his eyes, asking where she's been.

Where she's always been: needing him to come find her.

That night her singing is less than magnificent. Who says if you feel the blues you're gonna sing 'em all that much better? More Bessie Smith mythology. . . . After the gig, Harry leaves her on her own, he has to do some business with local musicians, so she goes alone to the hotel, where Hattie says to come have a drink. After a while Skate shows up, saying, "I got it, Hattie," before he sees Lela in the room.

Hattie says, "Never mind, Skate. It's no surprise to Lela what we do."

Lela watches while Skate gets out his kit, the spoon and candle and needle and strip of rubber hose. He cooks one up for Hattie while the black woman stretches out her left arm, feeling for a good vein. So far, the arm has only a thin pale-blue scar against the coffee color of the inside of her arm. Lela's seen Skate. He's a map of the Northern Pacific Railroad, the skin on his arms and thighs gone taut from punctures. Even his belly is slightly silvered, almost like stretchmarks in the right lamplight. She watches Hattie shoot it up and when the horse kicks in she nods with it, leaning back her head and letting it drop; leaning, dropping, her eyes neither opened nor closed, no muscle left to do either job. On the nod, Skate calls it. Hattie's there.

The saxophone player cooks up another one in the same spoon, then rolls up his sleeve and pumps a fist, getting up the blood. Noticing Lela in the corner, he turns toward her. "You still here?"

Not a question needing an answer.

"If you want to come along," he adds, "this one's on me."

Something else to hide from Harry. Another taste of that apple.

"It don't mean nothing, the first one. Just a chip is all."

Still wearing her nightclub dress, no sleeve to roll upward, she offers her arm to Skate, who bends and presses a thumb against her vein.

"Just a chip," she says. "Just for tonight." The words sound like lyrics to her next song.

This is where the song ends, but Lela's still singing. Dust on the needle and the last refrain skips back

". . . like broken glass   broken glass   broken glass . . ."

Valentine awakens and she's still there, in his bed. Three in the morning, she should have left hours ago.

"I didn't have the heart," she tells him. "I need sleep and I don't want to put my clothes on again."

Valentine tells her she's free to stay but she says otherwise. Harry's waiting.

In the taxi she can still smell Valentine. Opening the window wide, she washes herself with the wind.

As a child, Harry suffered from acute dyslexia, and his anxiety in the presence of the written word has never been entirely overcome. Though menus, street signs, and film credits pose no threat to his cool, he is unnerved by newspapers, uneasy in bookstores, and the arrival of a letter can undo him entirely. His own signature, if literally transcribed, would read HLr/, only slightly more meaningful to him than a simple X. Musical notes, crawling climbing jagged dots, can be more easily deciphered but they are no more music to him than a string of scratches, HLr/, is Harry Lord.

His mother, a doting only-parent, had misread (dyslectic in her own fashion) his malady, seeing in his difficulties with words (dyslexia leading logically to dysorthography) only a confusion of order, like some Arab mentality in which he wrote from right to left; droL yrraH. Since his only interest was the piano, upon which he could already pick out, with a single finger, every note from the treble clef of "Für Elise," and since she was a practical woman, she'd had the piano restrung and tuned anew, putting the bass notes to the right of middle C and the treble to the left, so that, from the time he was five years old, young Harry had a backward piano to play with, his left hand strolling out the melodies that his right hand anchored with bass. Later, when no music school would have him, his compositions illegible and his need for a backward piano incomprehensible, he'd stuck with his own music, though conceding the game and retraining himself through three painful years on a normal keyboard.

The wounds of the reorientation have never healed. He has a more talented and flexible left hand than most but his right hand retains the clumsiness that is ill-fitting on a jazz virtuoso. His compositions are thus invariably original, including some of the most astounding bass arpeggios ever recorded, but there are those who argue that his keyboard accompaniments place a hindrance on Lela Maar, that her natural range is undermined by a busy, low, and sonorous something that leaves a gaping silence in the heart of the heart of the song.

Besides singing chorus in the band, Hattie is makeup girl, secretary, and camp follower, and it is she who reads the reviews to Harry, sparing him the dual anxieties of print and prejudice, promising to skip over the bad parts and read aloud only the words of praise or disinterested commentary. He receives mail from music teachers (love you, hate you), aspiring pianists, fans, and occasional devotees, and Hattie reads these letters to him as well, censoring nothing, most especially not the letters from irate blacks telling him Lela's stolen their style and that he is white trash, or worse, for letting her do it.

Early in December, while reactions to "From Here to Tuesday" are still coming in, Harry opens a batch of mail and passes the letters over to Hattie. The first few are fan letters, we like the song, whyn't you do some more blues like "Slow Train Don't Come"?, a prayer from a Midwestern parish priest suggesting that Lela cut a Christian hymn, a confused and overscholarly analysis of Harry's chord structures that Hattie has trouble reading, and then an oddity: a poster folded in half, announcing a rally to provide assistance to the Jews of Europe. Time: 9 PM. Date: Dec 12. Place: St. Mark's in the Bowery. Bring Money Bring Hope Bring a Pair of Willing Hands. Atop the poster is a Star of David with a crucifix running through it.

Harry says, "Are you sure it's addressed to me?"

Hattie digs around for the envelope. "Harry Lord, Composter. Must be you."

"Composter?"

"Not everbody can write like us, Harry. Hey, they's a letter inside. You must a missed it."

Unlike the reviews, Hattie reads the letters aloud, seldom reading ahead to see what might need censoring. Thus it is from her mouth that Harry hears the words and understands them long seconds before she does: "You think your wife's in love with you? Go to the rally and you'll see the other man."

He wonders if his hands, laced by clenched fingers into a single fist, will ever separate. "No signature, I suppose."

Hattie, her comprehension spreading across her face in slow wrinkles like a smile, says, "Nope. No initials neither."

A few days later, Hattie breaks the news to Lela: "Harry knows."

"Harry," exhaling, "know what?"

" 'Bout your fella. The FBI told him."

For three nights she sleeps uneasily at his side, eyes searching the part in the curtains, to the fire escape and beyond Manhattan's lights, writing lyrics for herself that will make him understand what she has always understood, ever since the first night she'd gone to his place and sung for him and made love to him and gone to get her dresses and shoes while he'd slept. The night Solomon had hanged himself and Fingers had cut the heart from her, saying it was her, it was her, it was her.

Harry feigns sleep, tossing, seeking comfort while getting tighter and more wounded with each minute of passing silence.

Sitting up in bed, Lela whispers, All right, then, say it, *say* it, but Harry rips a sigh from his hiding place on the other side of the bed so she goes on whispering to him—is it aloud or only to herself?—Now, Harry, from the beginning, what's between you and me is this jazz blood, a current that moves forever in the same direction, undulating the night and day. Not simple love, not mandolins, not clarinets . . . Are you listening? I sing what you play and what you play is something Pied Piperish to me, I come right out of my skin, and that's more than love, now, isn't it, Harry? Or if not *more* than love at least a different kind of loving. It's your music and it's you as well, the way you take me on a train, standing me up against the swaying wall and pushing up my skirt like that. I sing *you*, Harry, and that's more marriage than most people have, now, ever, even in their most elaborate daydreams, Harry. . . .

She awakens at noon, not remembering when she gave in to sleep, or how, or what Harry had heard. He has been to the piano and gone, the first scratches of a new song not yet dried on the sheet, no lyrics yet, nothing for Lela to rewrite, She sits at the keyboard and picks out the treble with one finger, notes falling from a dizzying height into a black pool somewhere south of middle C, getting dangerously below her range.

Harry comes in with a newspaper, cigarettes, a clutch of fresh roses, nothing in his face to say the night has changed them. "To work," he says, and they begin going over the new number, a deadly slow piece of business remindful of what he was up to before Lela, and all this time she is swinging her voice upward and downward, wondering if he'd heard her in the night or if he'd been asleep. Harry goes on playing, wearing his left hand to a frazzle with a series of bass runs right out of Chopin's bad moods, and only when she asks him if he's got a name for it and he says "No mandolins, no clarinets" does she know that he heard every word of her confessions.

PAGES OF THE ARCHIVES

1 NEW YORK 1961

Armand was dead, that was a fact. He and my stepmother, Elaine. It hadn't been pretty. They'd had to cut away a piece of Armand's skull to extract it from the steering wheel upon which he'd apparently fallen asleep at ninety-five mph. Elaine had leaped through the windshield to meet her Maker and had left her legs behind. Someone from Westchester had done a hell of a job of sewing her back together before the burial.

The whole affair was closed-coffin, which suited me just fine.

An uncle I hardly knew took charge of things. When I'd been younger his wife had referred to me as the changeling, which I later learned was her polite way of calling me a bastard. The uncle was named Darren, call me Day. "As you know, your father and I weren't friendly with each other. Too much blood over the dam, I suppose. Anyway, I've been named executor of his will. Have you ever read it?"

There was money enough for school and beyond. I wouldn't be counting my coppers for another ten years or so.

Day said something about Columbia being a good choice for college but I told him all I felt like doing was getting out from under.

"To where?"

"The West. Europe, maybe. Or maybe South America."

"And during these travels," Day wanted to know, "how will you make a living?"

"I have my devices."

"Drug-dealing? Pimping?"

"What's it to you?"

"Don't get riled, Hunter. I just want you to keep your nose clean."

I was seventeen and already was growing annoyed with my life. You get your heart set on something and it takes its sweet time showing up. I turned to picture-taking to impress the art types I was prone to run around with. A Taoist sculptor engaged in creating a stone-soul. An accordionist trying to fuse cool jazz with dance-hall music from the Belle Epoque. Alcoholic actors debating the morality of Method.

"To be is to act."

"To play is to be."

"Acting *is*."

I had a girlfriend, Esther, who read Tarot cards the way others read the sports pages. In the cards there was always winning and losing, and her favorite was the Hanged Man. We used an action painter's studio whenever we wanted to make it, and while she sprawled on the floor, her hair in disarray across a field of sprinkled paint, discarded squirt guns littering the place, and the floor itself resembling Pollock's overlaid works, I'd see *her* as ism'd in a female fashion. She was a costumed nude reciting primal free verse and I screwed every card in her deck, she was one hell of a work of art.

It was Esther who first talked about origins. "I know my whole past," she said, "even from the day I was born. My father took pictures. My mother in labor, the birth, the afterbirth. Those pictures tell me everything I can't remember for myself."

It was the times. America's children were being pressed to ask unanswerable questions. A first generation under the bomb. Tomorrow we might be erased like the wrong answer to a formula. Back to the origins, sifting therefore through the sandbox of history for ancient toys, spare change, dogshit, identity.

"There's something else for you," Day told me. "It wasn't mentioned in the will but it's obvious that it's for you."

Armand's archive of Lela Maar.

Letters from Valentine. Fan mail. Unfinished poetry.

Lyric sheets in her own hand.

Newspaper clippings, posters, magazine articles.

Yellowing sheet music with gray notes (pencil) between the bars. A code presumed to be her breathing pattern.

A dozen books on her life and music.

Photographs, some of them signed. She usually dropped the a in Lela and the r in Maar: Lel Maa.

Armand's correspondence to England and throughout America.

All of her records, even the rarities.

Her jewelry; two evening gowns; a lone white glove.

I'd never seen any of it. Tracking down my mother had been Armand's hobby and it seemed he'd been obsessed. Holding that glove in my hand was a shock, like touching her pale fingers, a trace of vanishing skin. Going through her things, it took me a long time to realize that he'd done it for me. His kindness. He had always insisted that he wasn't my father but my guardian; I was to call him Armand.

I read everything but when I was finished I wasn't sure what I'd read. It was like circling a house in search of a door but there isn't one and even the windows are boarded up. She was a Leo with Scorpio rising; that doesn't say much. I kept on reading, waiting to smell something more than the mustiness of those pages. She's my mother and she might have left a lamp lit in the window. Here's a fact: using her real name as a cover, she had an abortion in 1936. The doctor wrote *boy* in blue pen under Comments. Somewhere between him and me she had changed her mind about these matters.

When I was seventeen I had plenty of time on my hands. Day was still talking up Columbia and I said I might later but not just yet. I spent the first few months after high school holed up in my room with those archives, pawing through the papers and listening to the music. I felt I was getting somewhere, and that was my first false start. Once, I called up a man whose name kept appearing in the biographies to ask him what she was like.

"A good person," he told me. "A real sweetheart. Don't believe the trash people wrote. She was a saint."

"I mean, who she was. Not her virtues."

"She was a lady and she sang like an angel. There's not much more to tell you, kid."

"I need something more."

"More I don't have. She's been dead a long time, you know."

"Right. All my life."

That's a fact to fret over, seeing my birthdate in those books written up as her deathdate. So much of the rest was made up but that much I can't gloss over.

When I'd read everything ten times and memorized all of her melodies, the ache had taken hold of me somewhere around the chest and there was no way to cough it up. Armand had done a job but he hadn't found the man, though he'd nearly laid a finger on time and place and it seemed to say England, 1943. Weeks went by and I was drifting away. Day called one night to tell me I was courting failure. I agreed with him and took to the road.

2

LONDON

Crossing my first street, I was nearly creamed by a cabbie with Grand Prix intentions. The streets of the West End, unmatrixed, seemed to be leading nowhere special, and the darkness was somehow dirty. The first person to address me was, no surprise, a prostitute.

"Ten quid for an hour's slap and tickle? That's cheap for a Yank, exchange rates being what they are."

I said I wasn't interested. "I'm looking for my mother."

"I've heard this before."

"You'd be surprised."

"No, I wouldn't. Off with you, then. Cheers."

Moving away, I had the momentary sensation of walking through time. Not the linear version, with plus and minus signs over future and past, but a simple ticking-off of seconds as well as footsteps, though it may have been the neon flickering above my head or the rumble of the Underground, the Piccadilly Line beneath the pavement. I decided I was run down, that the archive had me bugged, wired, plugged into a cosmos that was no longer there. Inventory time. I am walking on cement, cracked and litter-strewn. Above and to each side are iron grateworks, either balconied or barred windows. Tailpipes breathing on my knees. My passport tucked against my right lung, safe. This Nikon, fully loaded, hanging round my neck.

I ordered fish and chips in a stand-up joint off Leicester Square, then sat on a pigeon-sprinkled bench to eat. Theatergoers, chatting gaily, passed me by, a few of them looking my way distractedly. I seemed to be disturbing the landscape. It's my clothes, I thought, thoroughly spooked. I must look like a lost tourist or a derelict. Stuffing the last of my uneaten fish into a trashcan, I crossed the square and ducked into a street of zany theater lights, screaming marquees, muttering billboards.

I lit off to where I'd spoken with the prostitute, meaning to tell her I'd been sincere, that I truly *was* looking for my mother and not in any Oedipal sense. Armand had done so much work and now it was my turn. I was in London because of her and that was looking enough.

But the prostitute was gone. Hired, purchased, vanished. Slapping and tickling elsewhere. I waited around for almost an hour before my courage ran out; then I walked a circular route back to my hotel, up the stairs, through a numbered door, and fell fully clothed, already asleep, onto the bed.

They'd called them *flying bombs* at the time. *Rocketry* had been a science-fiction term, something for eggheads or the funny papers. I pored over piles of photographs of the afterward, mounds of rubble, windows like open mouths of flame, floors and ceilings bowed or collapsed, stacked like torn playing cards, plaster, powder, smoke, helmeted men lifting limp, corpse-filled dresses, various nests of rock, shards of porcelain or glass or bone. Some of the photographs showed the rockets in flight, V1 or V2, the prints, grainy and obscure, of broad-winged, black, and ponderous arrows suspended in grayness. Around noon, about the time a records clerk was telling me it was time to close up for lunch, I came across a photo I was looking for. Caption in scribble of black ink: "Ruin of St. Jude Emergency Hosp. 19 Sept 1944." My birthday. Taken from some nearby window or rooftop, it showed a rough horseshoe of rubble round a crater strewn with beds, chunks of wall, bodies, and little fires like votive candles burning here and there. In the foreground, a knot of uniformed men leaning over a stretcher; on the horizon, billows of smoke, firefighters, a pair of overturned cars. The photograph had been taken at night and was a mass of intersecting shadows. Leaning over the table until my nose nearly touched it, I examined the image millimeters at a time, finding a hand, an outstretched leg, silhouettes impossible to define as man or woman, shadows that might or might not have contained a dead woman and a living child.

Folding the picture once, I slipped it into my shirt: my own first entry into the archive.

At the Royal Archives I had the sensation that I'd already seen those photos. It was impossible after a time to distinguish one ruin from another. One body, dead in its print dress, was the same as another in its pajamas. Many of the pictures were faded, sepia, as if having been improperly exposed, and my fingers grew sticky with chemicals, carbon, paper cuts, and the dust of that sunless room.

I took my case to an assistant archivist, a tweedy, balding man with eyeglasses balanced at the tip of his nose. He lit one Player's after another and his ashtray was brimming.

"To locate an individual, a single person from all of history, is far from impossible. The police do it all the time. But don't count on names of women. Interchangeable and all. Women marry, divorce. Remarry. Go back to maiden names or keep husbands' surnames merely for legal ends."

Though I hadn't asked, I was offered tea, something to swallow with my hope.

"I want to look anyway," I said.

"And if you find out who your father was, what will it serve you?"

"To know."

"And nothing more. What if he was a criminal? Would he be any less anonymous to you? To find a name, an address, an occupation. I could write all of these things on an index card for you, add a few details such as color of eyes, height, distinguishing marks, then dirty the card up a bit to make it look *old*, wander across to some other archive, missing persons or what-have-you, slip the card into the proper file, and ta-da: tomorrow you have found your father."

"But it wouldn't be the truth."

The archivist leaned forward and the overhead light glinted in his bifocals. "Young man, who ever said that history had to be the truth?"

She hadn't been at the hospital when it had burned down. There'd been a second V2 that night, reaching a mile or so up the road to the corner of Exton and Secker streets to our ambulance. Tracing my finger over the Lambeth grid of the London map, I found that the corner was just up Waterloo Road from the hospital, in the direction of the Thames. An incident report for flying bomb AC190944 listed the names of the dead: *Masters, Roger*, and *Unidentified*. An appendix of Armand's spade work included evidence that traced Unidentified to Ariel Mason and then linked Ariel Mason to Lela Maar. The final police deposition was dated 26 October 1946, when the last link was made.

Attached to the incident report were several photographs. Only two were of any use to me, the others showing nothing but gray-blank ruin, darkness, more of that anonymous rubble. In one of the photos there was an overturned lorry in the foreground, flame coming from the cab, two helmeted men hosing it down. In the background, partly obscured by plumes of smoke, was the shattered stained-glass window of a church. In the second photo, there was more. This time, a back view of the lorry, surrounded by fire, and figures frozen, running either to or from the fire. With a magnifying glass, I examined this photo from top to bottom, making out the face of what looked to be a soldier heading toward the lorry, wisps of smoke, leaves of flame, a woman leaning from a nearby window, mouth opened in a small o of horror. And then, in the bottom-right corner, what would have been a patch of street only a few yards from the lorry, the crook of a man's arm. On the arm a Red Cross patch, the ✚ showing clearly against a white field. The man's neck and shoulder, the shadow of a hip. He seems to be missing an eye. And in the crook of his arm, obscured by shadows and the chaos of low-quality film, the head of a child: me.

Mother and son, but no father in sight. Ariel Mason had arrived at the clinic in June, signing in with the false name but presenting ID with the real one. No mention anywhere of where she'd come from, just why. A reformed drug addict, more than six months pregnant at the time, seeking sanctuary. A surviving nurse remembered nothing of her. "There was a war on. We knew everybody but we never got too close. There wasn't time for that, you understand."

No wonder Armand gave up. After a month I grew sick of it and could no longer bear the idea of descending yet another stairway into an evil-smelling basement filled with dead leaves and faded calligraphies, codes, typing errors, perforate seals, decaying carbons, rusting paper clips, broken staples, file clasps, receipts Scotch-taped to certificates, reports, triplicate forms, visas, stamps, tampered locks, mildewed dossiers, name lists, indices and cross-references. Filling out an entry application, my mother had left the father's name blank. Her choice. I can only assume she meant to tell me later, thinking later would be just around the corner. She couldn't know that her history would finally be written on the dead shavings from trees, papyrus, and that if someone held a match to a single sheet of paper her entire lifetime would fade from view eternally and succumb to a lacy and windblown species of ash.

I realized I could spend my life getting pissed off or I could roll with the punches and stop wondering. So it had to be mythology.

I got the hell out of London. But I kept my souvenirs for the archives.

3

PARIS

In bed she was a screamer, a crooner, an acrobat, an actress. She wanted me to say things to her, dirty things, in English, and was angry when I couldn't come up with more than simple naughties, fuckscrew, the usual. At thirty, Isabelle had already catalogued a hundred lovers, she said, and I could at worst provide continuity, a few notches on the bedpost or X's on the coital calendar.

"I learned English from a soldier in Grenoble who liked for me to kiss his *zizi*. I was a kid and did it well." She had read about Colette and intended to live a similar life, though money was a problem. "I have to dress in order to undress. What I am not wearing is only interesting if I've worn it. Do you follow?"

I followed her into the bedroom and she looped her legs round my shoulders, taking me in as deep as I could go, shouting something to me in French, but I didn't know if it was *harder*, *deeper*, *faster*, *softer*, *longer*, or what. I managed.

She and her friends stuck together like moths circling a hazy light bulb. On the move, Clignancourt to Clichy, Jean's place or Giselle's, up north to Saint-Ouen and then down the long slope again to Isabelle's place at La Fourche. The fork, literally. They avoided the renowned stream of talky, philosophical Paris, the spotlit corners of Saint-Germain and Saint-Michel, those huddles of published thinkers and their disciples. They'd read the papers, Thierry and the others, and hadn't yet seen articles about themselves. Of course: the new movement always begins in obscurity. The wheel of the sun will always turn up some excuse for failure.

Isa, too. She had her moods. An out-of-work actress who spent long hours gazing out her bedroom window to the dull cement courtyard below: a drainpipe, garbage bin, two opaque windows to someone else's loo. No consolation in this geometry, no inspiration. She was letting me stay with her because I helped her level off into a void. I was amusing, she said, and at least I already knew how to fuck. For a week she'd been dragging me through streets and endless evenings from one trashy apartment to another, walls postered and wrinkled with cracks, cockroaches skittering over books lying open-faced on linty rugs, broken windows patched over with cardboard, arguments rising from the fumes of alcohol, and collaborated group poetry written on someone's bedsheet with Isa's red lipstick. And always Thierry, soulful, jealous Thierry, watching my every move.

"So who is he?" I asked her one day while she was brooding near her window.

"He is no one who used to be someone. You don't need to be afraid."

"He's got a knife."

"He would never dare to use it. On himself, perhaps."

"He makes me nervous. Let's skip tonight's party and find a restaurant somewhere."

She said she didn't feel like it, she felt like staying home. "I've got, you know, *le cafard*." *Cafard* being French for *cockroach*, also meaning the blues.

And she had it something fierce. I took off my clothes and joined her in bed but she wasn't interested. "The times are such hell," she said.

"Are they?"

"Perhaps not in America. But in France . . ." The refrigerator hummed and there was that sound of a motor kicking in. "In France, we have no politicians, no artists, no theater. I am an actress and have nothing to act. Nothing that is written anymore is worth interpreting."

"Is that all it is?"

"All what?"

"Your blues. Your *cafard*."

She gave me a smile that said I was an asshole. "You barely know me. You must think I am only a girl; cunt, *nénés*. Or, like Thierry, you would like to crawl into the hole of me and hide. Men never know me, not really. Men interpret me as I interpret a role. And you, I picked you up on the street like an art object, *un objet trouvé*, and have been wearing you around like cheap jewelry for nearly a week. How can you know my blues?"

She cried for a while, softly and without heartbreak. I didn't know how to console her so I consoled myself, caressing her breasts, kissing her neck, partaking of her silver lining. "I am having," she sniffed, "a terrible year. There is my mother, who is dead last winter. And Thierry, whom I cannot love. I am unemployed. And there is Algeria.

"I worry about death," Isa continued. "Death, not dying. In every paper—every day, it seems—there are numbers of dead, places, and crazy reasons for dying. This morning I read of an Arab girl in Oran who wore a plastique in her vagina. She pretended to be a whore and when an officer bent to take her, she blew up."

I took a long pull from a wine bottle. "We'll need more of this," I said.

"Not for me."

I drank alone, killing the bottle.

Later, she gave in to sex; then we rose from the bed and dressed and took the métro to the Porte de Clignancourt, where Giselle had a studio that overlooked the flea market. The usual faces were there with more bottles of wine, Being and Nothingness 1961, passing, passing, passing.

Isa's *cafard* had affected me and I spent most of the evening and the night that followed between drunkenness and anger. For a brief moment, Thierry happened by with a glass of cognac for the Yank, as well as advice: "You thought you could help her. You can't. Leave her to me."

"You and your knife."

"The knife's not for her, it's for you."

Searching out a cozy corner, I slept but refused to dream.

A nudge on my shoulder woke me, a hand passing a stick of hashish.

Why in hell not? Across the room, Thierry was putting a move or two on Isa but she was having none of it. Alain was busy organizing a trip to Algeria, where the hash was said to have come from, and was getting enthusiastic responses from the guitar player, Giselle, Jean-Luc, and a few others.

"What about you, Page?"

"I'll go if Isa goes." Brave words.

Everyone had a different opinion of when the war had started: 1945 or 1953? At Sétif or in Bône? For years now the French and Algerians had been engaged in *main-à-main*, throat slitting (what the Arabs called the Big Smile), plastic bombs in nightclubs cutting the legs from dancers, and even the French army planning a Paris coup to rid the nation of its traitors. I was a teenager still and believed everything they said to me, these eighteenth-*arrondissement artistes*. They made the war zone sound like a dance hall for small-time poets, and who was I to argue overmuch?

I had a hit of smoke to seal the bargain, a glass of brandy to wash it down, and then slept again with my head against my knees, a pillow of rocks. The next time I awakened I was in a taxi bound for the Avenue de Clichy, my head resting in the crook of Isabelle's arm. She asked if I was feeling any better.

"Better than what?"

"You tried to beat up Thierry."

"Did I win?"

"No."

"Then don't tell me what happened."

When we were in bed, I tried to get myself into the mood for her but it wasn't in me. I imagined her legs twining around my own, her teeth on my neck, her language, the smell of her. No dice.

"Don't worry, Page. Sleep now. We've got plans to make in the morning."

I told her I made no plans. I lived from day to day.

She placed a nipple in my mouth to shut me up. Still hovering over me, she said, "We're going to the source, Page. The place of dying."

I twirled my tongue round her nipple and it stiffened on cue. Reaching a hand, I found she was wet. Four in the morning, drunk, and Isa wants it.

I got down to serious business. Wheeling woman and dealing man.

"You'll come with me," she said. "*Mon ange guardien*. We'll go *there*."

A breeze parted the curtains, bringing with it the smell of decayed fruit. I rolled her onto her back, mounting her while there still was time. She took all of me at once, gasping, then continued, saying she needed me with her, something about a role to play, a part, stage directions, living theater. "All of my nightmares, Page. All of my blues."

I worked on her, heaving and hoing, trying to hold in check the cognac that burned my blood and left me weak. She raised her hips to meet me, talking across the dark in both French and English, whatever came to mind. *Rutting*, I thought. That was the word for it. Hands clapping in the dark. Jumping and shivering in space, no sparks.

4

MARSEILLE

Marseille under summer rain. Vendors in the fish market covering up with newspapers, hordes of flies moving in under tarpaulins and tents, the sky pale and yellowish, streaked black with clouds blown northward across the Mediterranean. The surf left a vapor along the old port as the boats bobbed in a rising tide. Taking cover in a portside café, I ordered a beer for myself and a pastis for Isa from a waiter with the filthiest bib I had ever seen. "Nice town," I said.

"Decayed," Isa answered. "Our wartime and colonial heritage. Look around you, this city is hardly French anymore."

The *pieds noirs* were coming home. *Black feet*, those French born elsewhere, these from North Africa. The war was lost and the Arabs were forcing out all the Europeans. They were coming from Oran and Algiers, Bougie and Bône, a dozen boats a day filled with empty-eyed women clutching suitcases, twined boxes, candelabras, photographs of relatives lost in the shuffle that they passed from waiter to waiter—Have you seen him? her? them?—and cramming into dockside cafés to wait for other boats to arrive, staring anxiously off to the south, from where they came. French soldiers remained in Algeria to fight ultra renegades as well as the FLN, but the war was lost and everyone knew it except those ultra generals who had gone into hiding with what was left of their Organisation de l'Armée Secrète, the OAS. The throat-cutting was far from ended. Thousands in Algeria were smiling widely, and the exodus of the *pieds noirs* had only just begun.

I had booked passage for the two of us on a boat called *Les Bras du Monde*, a crusted hulk with a half-dozen passenger cabins that would first stop at Alicante in Spain before shoving off for Algiers. Giselle, Alain, and the others had all changed their minds about the voyage. Push coming to shove, only Page and Isa had any real desire to visit a war, it didn't matter how much hash could be scored off the street. "Algiers is the worst," Giselle had said, advising us to try Oran. "It's mostly European, not that many Arabs. And the OAS is mostly in Algiers." All the more reason for Isa to insist on Algiers. Her death wish was getting serious.

"I suppose you'll find a hotel in the Casbah," said Alain. "Where they'll serve you croissants and plastiques for breakfast."

"Not Isa," Giselle said. "She's more direct. She'll want to go dancing at that nightclub that's been blown up, how many times is it? Four? Five?"

"Isa could dance all night."

"Change your mind, Isa? Stay home and fall slowly apart with the rest of us?"

If it was a joke, it was not funny anymore. I'd have preferred to go to Oran. "You know, Isa. The beach scene."

But all during the train ride south she'd babbled about going to the source, where the dying was. Sitting in the bar car, draining one beer after another, she grew progressively more incoherent. I followed her brew for brew, past Lyon, Beaune, down the Midi to Avignon, and when at dawn the train pulled into the Saint-Charles station at Marseille I practically had to carry her from the bar, slinging her suitcase and my duffel bag over one shoulder and supporting her with my free arm. The rain had begun to fall. "Perfect," she murmured. "Splendid. The weather all fevered, hot. I prayed for this."

Checking into a hotel near the old port, we slept off the beer and I decided not to forget the whole thing after all. Isa, sobered, felt like having sex, and afterward she was calmer, less morbid. I had a way of fucking her back to a level plane that was, if not sanity, at least not rabid lunacy. We had a long lunch in a nearby café, veal and potatoes and red wine, then picked up the tickets for the boat, which was leaving the next afternoon. After another visit to the hotel bed, we returned to the café to kill time. When Isa again began to talk about the trip, all the gee-whiz death we'd be seeing, I cut her short. "I don't want to hear about it."

She brooded for a moment over her pastis. "I thought you understood."

"Well, maybe I don't."

"Then why did you agree to come along?"

"Who's with whom? I bought my own ticket."

"Answer the question. In good English."

She wanted the words and I wanted the images. I had a camera and she had pens and a spiral notebook. I admitted I was curious to see the war.

"I knew it!"

"But not like you. Not just the dying."

She wanted to know what else there was to war and I couldn't say I knew. Maybe London had done me in, all those pictures of the afterward.

"I don't really know what I'll do when we get there," I admitted. "I may never even make it off the boat."

"You flip."

"*Flop*. The word is *flop*. Read my lips."

She was disgusted with me. "After all our plans, our dreaming. Now you change your mind?"

"You're getting strange on me, Isa. Funny in the head."

"In my head, yes. Where I am hurting, wounded."

I suppressed a smile but it sneaked through to daylight. "It's only a paper cut, Isabelle."

"Stop twisting what I say. I am going to Algeria to get away from books, from words. To get close to the dying. Not that daily dying in Paris but the dying where babies burn, not *poupées*. Where life isn't a play or a movie."

"Did you memorize this or are you making it up as you go along?"

Her gaze was level. "I'll go alone if you prefer. On another boat."

I said that might not be a bad idea.

She sat motionless for long seconds, then reached forward and tipped her pastis onto the table; what was left in the glass spilled cold onto my lap. Then she reached for her bag, rose, gave me a last look that said *Straight to hell,* and left the café. I slapped a bill onto the table, stood up as though to go after her, then thought better of it and sat back down. Wherever she was going, it wouldn't be far enough. Brushing the pastis from my lap, I watched as she disappeared into the yellow August rain.

In a blue-lit bar on the edge of the old city, two accordionists wheezed out some Piaf tune while two disconsolate hookers went to work on me. I was sitting at a corner table thinking I'd drink myself silly before facing what promised to be a long night in a hotel room with a suicidal Frenchwoman.

The bar smelled of urine and Gauloise butts, and the accordions were giving me a headache. One of the hookers kept up her spiel in franglais, offering, as best I could figure out, a pipe, a pump, some coo, the business. Saying I didn't speak French didn't get me off the hook. "A blow? My ass? We fuck?" When I emptied my pockets, producing a comb, some coins, and a frazzle of lint, she let me be, but the other one, silent all the while, gazed mournfully across the table at me, her painted eyes looking bruised.

"*Fous le camp,*" I told her, one of the few phrases I'd mastered. "Get lost." But as faithful, or as witless, as a dog, she remained across from me, staring, her hands on display before her and her elbows planted like trees into the table's dark wood.

Paradox: the whisky made me sober. I felt like a kid and remembered I was not yet eighteen. This kind of revelation should happen to no one, ever. For long moments I wished I were back with Esther on that action painter's floor, trying to peel off her clothes, instead of watching this morose prostitute gaze into my shirtsleeves. I smoked my last cigarette like a joint, sucking out a long, hot ash and blowing smoke toward the prostitute's face. She didn't even blink. I dragged deeply and blew again: still nothing. Amazing. The other prostitute wandered back to me and laced an arm round my shoulder, then asked me if I didn't have at least enough to buy her a drink.

"Watch this," I told her. And again I blew smoke into the prostitute's eyes and with the same result.

The other prostitute only smiled, her mouth like an open wound. She gestured for me to lean across the table and look carefully into the woman's eyes. "All. Look at all."

I peered into dark irises, seeing nothing special.

"She is from Algeria," the woman told me. "A *pied noir*. She was left to watch over a group of young children but she fell asleep. The FLN came in the night and cut the children's throats. So the *pieds noirs* cut away her eyelids. Look closely."

Bending near to the woman, my nose nearly touching hers, I could smell the oil on her skin and hear the low rumble of her breathing. At the tops of her eyes were thin yellow scars, like half-moons, no lashes, only a pink stain of flesh.

"Maybe you should go now," the other woman told me. "Your bottle is gone and you have no money for me. Leave Alina alone. It's been a long time since she could fall asleep."

I slept dreamlessly, and when I awakened, just past dawn, I could hear falling water. Opening one eye, I saw Isa at the sink, her back to me as she peered into the mirror and put on her face. Bottle-green eyelids, scarlet mouth. She made herself up for a devouring, of time or of me. The mirror over the sink was cracked, and her reflection, from *my* angle, was torn into parts, her eyes askew as in some Picasso portrait: that weeping woman, teeth tearing at a hanky while one eye is a cup overflowing with tears.

Isa left the water running while she put on her clothes, jeans, a shirt belonging to yours truly, some cheap jewelry. Then, taking her purse but leaving her suitcase behind, she went out the door. When I was certain she wouldn't come back right away, I left the bed to turn off the running water and found that the handle had come away from the screw. I stood for long minutes with that handle in my hands and watched the water flow down the drain. Then I went back to bed and slept a less-than-tranquil sleep, awakening at ten minutes to noon to a pounding that could only be the manager. Checkout time at noon. Did I wish to stay another night?

Dragging myself up from the mattress, I began to put on yesterday's clothes. No sign of Isa, but her suitcase was there. Water was still running into the sink, a perpetual fall and gurgle, and looking out the window I saw that the rain had let up. The sky was white with something of blue beyond it, like an underpainting, and the port was calm, only a few boats coming in and out, lazy gulls swooping at their wakes.

I was downstairs just after noon to pay my bill and my change was less than I'd expected.

"There was also the phone call," the manager explained.

"What phone call?"

"Your lady friend called Paris."

"When? This morning?"

"No, last evening." He checked his receipt. "At six o'clock. She talked for eighteen minutes."

I didn't have time to speculate. The boat was leaving in another hour, and I took a taxi around the old port to the passenger dock. Both tickets were still in my duffel bag, as was the rest of my money. After boarding, I was led to a tiny, cramped cabin, just a hammock and closet really, where I left Isa's suitcase and my bag on the floor. I locked the door, then went back to the tide wall to keep an eye out for her.

A scavenger was making his way up and down the docks, picking up rags, ends of discarded rope, bits of useless metal, and other riffraff, stowing everything in a large canvas sack. He reminded me of the rummies in New York; wealth, like beauty, being in the eye of the beholder. When he approached the boat, I asked him what he planned to do with his treasures.

"*J'vais les vendre.*" Gonna sell 'em.

"How much?"

"*Bon marché.*" Cheap.

There were only ten more minutes until the boat was to leave. Isa was by this time halfway up the Midi, heading for Lyon, her thoughts spiraling round Thierry, fucking, art, death. I remembered for the first time in a week that I'd come to look for my father, but that was too much to think about at the moment. I had to leave a tip behind; *some*body had to see me off.

Returning to my cabin, I fetched Isa's suitcase and offered it to the scavenger. The old guy didn't understand what I was up to and it was hard to tell him in simple words. I was talking Indian: "Me give. You. Yours." He got the drift and together we pried the suitcase open. There were clothes, mostly, and a few newspapers. The old man pawed through jeans, skirts, blouses, and underthings, holding each of the articles to his nose in appraisal.

"Don't forget this," I told him, handing him Isa's boat ticket.

"*Pour aller en Algérie?*" To go to Algeria?

I nodded.

"*Je ferai mieux de vendre un billet à l'enfer.*" I'd have better luck selling a ticket to hell.

Nothing left to give away and nothing left to wait for, I got on board. As the ship was crawling out of the harbor, I stood on the deck and looked backward toward Europe, half expecting to see a taxi come screaming up to the dock and Isa stepping out, too late for the crossing to the other side of life. But there was no taxi. There were only scattered immigrants, diving gulls, a few out-of-work fishermen, and one old man sitting next to a suitcase, holding a pair of women's panties to his face and laughing hysterically into them.

My life had taken a turn for the worse so I did what unimaginative boys my age are wont to do. I went to war.

LELA MAAR SINGS HARRY LORD

"ELISIONS"

(4:41)

1942

When it happened, when I knew it was happening, I was saying to myself the world must be comin apart and if it ain't then I must be havin some kind of rainy spell or else I'm died and gone a bus stop closer to heaven. That's how it was to listen to a sound only my heart could make before but my hands couldn't think to play. I was leanin over a third beer up at Monroe's when Monk, who was only a sideman that night, started doing his number. It was the first time I'd heard him but I'd been hearin about him for what seemed like forever and avoiding going to listen cause I'd been workin on my own riffs downtown and didn't want to get swamped in someone else's mysteries. My want of music was a personal bitch back then, 1941 or '42, and I was having this problem getting her straight.

These were back-and-forth times and a lot was going on at once. Glenn Miller and Woody Herman was rounding up big orchestras, like twenty-five pieces, and playing the sweetest little swing, but it was all full of patterns, you know, that old AABA put together so nice, and I could always tell what was comin seventeen bars off and not a single blessed surprise in any of it. Teedle-oh on them clarinets and da-da-daah with the horns. They was takin jazz away from us and givin it to white girls with pony tails. The earth mighta gotten real sad about then except along come Thelonious and Bud Powell, Bird and Dizzy, and later on Miles, to save my black soul from the sounds of that ever-whitenin music.

But you asked me a question and the answer is no. I don't think Lord ever sat in with Thelonious Monk, not before or after. They was different people, both of them. The Monk was a strange guy among a whole lot of strange guys, wearin his chains and dashikis and that little Chinese cap, and Lord was still Lord, moody as ever and maybe worse now that Lela was on the needle. Anyway, times was changed. Musicians couldn't just sit down with each other no more and start playin. You was in or you was out, you know what I'm sayin? We'd set up someplace and start workin through a number, and if someone else, someone not with us, stood up and tried to move in, we'd get as far away as possible, lookin out for chords and riffs no stranger could find all by himself. We was buildin cliques, yeah, but we was headed somewhere special and didn't want to get our music dragged back to swing and doo-dah. That's why you always hear about cats turning their backs to the crowd or walking off the scene when they wasn't on their solo. We was virtuosos and we had a lot to work out of our blood.

It was a real black time in those days but there was a few good whites around, like Lennie Tristano and Lee Konitz, and a course Lord. After he did "Elisions" and it worked for him, he fired most a the band and quit goin out on the road. Skate was with him like always, and Sammy Gray on drums. Slow Curt was the only stand-up bass I know who'd play with Lord. Following that man's left hand was a chore, and by that time, with less symphonic shit behind her, Lela had the room she always needed.

"Elisions" was the first piece a Harry's I could really crawl into and love. Scat singing was on its way in but Lela did something else, them half-words that made it sound like more than singing. *A'll voo* and *you'vemy*;

ha har hell instead of *Hard Heart Hotel.* Course they went downhill for the critics after that, but so did we all. And Lord really got his piano out a the shadows with "Elisions," all those hesitations and improvised arpeggios, like where the note should be but isn't so you hear it anyway, and then at the end when he plays *all* the notes and you know in your head you was hearing something *else* and what he gives you is even better. He surprised me there, that was a fine touch.

I run into them one night down around the Village in one a them basement joints where the sound held close to the head cause a the low ceiling and all. I got there in time for "Elisions," not the version you'll hear on the recording but their long side of it, like they was gonna play it all night if they felt like it. Lela was out a this world, I'd never heard such singing before. She was using Skate's run for a springboard, kicking off these vocal riffs and those half-words all up and down the place. Lord had his head bent down low to the keyboard like he needed to listen to himself a little or he might get blown away, and the club was all tensed up, people's heads nodding, fists clenchin and unclenchin, and I found I was doin it, too, sitting there in my chair playing right along with them, following as best as I could. They made solo rounds after a while, Skate to Lord to Sammy, back to Lord, then they all quit while Lela went into this humming and breathing number that sounded like a prayer and slowed the whole thing down to half-notes that slurred back and forth. None a this is on that recording and it's too bad, cause I guarantee you I saw tears coming out a Skate's eyes while he listened to Lela doing her stuff, and about the time Lord picked it up again with a soft riff and then Slow Curt scratched a note or two on his bass, I can't say with all honesty that mine was the driest eyes in the place.

"4 2 2 / A 3"

(6:12)

1943

The song, if you can call it that, has no lyrics whatsoever. Without them, at least a key word or two, Harry can't find a name for it.

"You've got to call it something," the man tells him. "I can't put out a blank jacket with no title. Who's gonna put their money down for that?"

Harry says to give him a minute. "I'll come up with something."

It is late in the evening and they've been in the studio since early afternoon. Hattie's gone out for sandwiches and beer and the musicians have skipped across the street for a shot of whisky at Calvin's. "Anybody seen Lela?"

No one has. She comes and goes like that, seldom says to or from where.

Harry, feeling tired for the first time that day, sits alone at his piano, staring for a long time at his hands, right and left. What they've just recorded is not at all what they'd meant to do. It was supposed to have been "Purges 1 and 2," a series of improvs built around a Lord composition, a few chord and tempo switches and five pages of lyrics for Lela to do whatever she felt with. Trouble is, nobody's up to it and everything that starts to become that piece becomes finally something else. An hour before, following a fine melody extemp from Skate's saxophone, they stumbled into a whole new sound, and whatever it was it was fine with all concerned. The man behind the glass says he's got a copy of it, do they want him to hold it for a master?

Harry only nods, looking at his hands.

"Just so you come up with a name for it." The soundman wants to know if they still plan on doing the "Purges" number. "We could make this other bit the B side."

Harry says they'll do "Purges 1 and 2" another time. "After the weekend. I think we all need a little break."

Hattie arrives with the beer and sandwiches, and Skate and Sammy drift in behind her. Slow Curt is already back in the studio packing away his bass.

"Ain't you hungry?" Hattie calls to him, but he doesn't hear her or isn't listening. She passes out the food and beer. "Where's Lela?"

Sammy says he hasn't seen her. Skate just shrugs.

Lord opens wide the studio door and blocks it with a chair to keep it open. They all can hear the playback of the last number and it seems to soothe the nerves that the lengthy session has frayed. Ever since "Elisions" they are not at all what they were. This new music of theirs is liberating but it is also soul-trying. Every gig requires a reach into somewhere painful or too distant or too close. Wounds and blessings are strewn along the way. Skate is off the junk at last and has grown a beard, become more thoughtful, introverted. When he speaks he is all punctuation and pause. He avoids Hattie, seeking out women who don't mind when he goes a whole night without saying a word or when, for no reason at all, he will get up and get dressed and walk out into the night and not come back. Slow Curt has dropped his old whack-and-thrum style and plays a more intense and measured bass, his brow creasing from the search, and he laughs less than he did when they were just playing good-times jazz and taking trains from club to club, meeting new women and shaking hands with men with lots of rings. "Cut deep," Skate says, meaning something close to get to the heart of it, and they spend many hours waiting to let out some ultimate beast in themselves, one and all nodding toward Lela as toward the setting sun. The music has become religion and all they can really do anymore is to let it play.

The playback is still going when the studio manager comes in with a clipboard and asks Harry to sign the release sheet. There is a typed form with all their past recordings written on it, alongside each of the titles that John Rose Ltd. has released. The studio manager has already filled in playing time, 6:12, and the next release number 422/A3, and Harry signs his name next to a blank where the title should be. Then he crosses out the notation "B side" and writes "A and B," instructing the sound man to use the remaining three and a half minutes of the piece as side B.

"No name for it?"

"Why not just leave it as it stands?"

While the musicians are packing away their instruments, Harry heads for the toilet. As he steps inside, a woman is coming out, one of the studio choir singers. She smooths her skirt with her hands and excuses herself. "The ladies' wasn't available and I waited the longest time."

Harry says it's OK and has started to close the door when she reaches out a hand to stop him. "Mr. Lord, I think it's your wife."

"What do you mean?"

The woman holds a thumb between index and middle fingers, miming a syringe.

"Where?" Harry asks. "In there?" Pointing at the other door.

The woman nods.

Harry tries the door but it is locked. He calls to Lela to open up. There is no answer.

Skate, standing behind him, says, "It wasn't me this time, Harry. I swear it, I've gone clean."

"Then where?"

"Search me. I been trying to keep an eye on her."

It takes five minutes to find the night watchman and another ten for him to shuffle through his mass of keys for the right one. They hurry back to the toilets and Harry slips the key into the lock, turning back the bolt. The door swings open and they find Lela seated on the toilet, her skirt pulled to her waist, head tipped back against the wall, her lids open to the barest sliver of eye, but when she opens her mouth to speak, something other than words or lyrics is all she can manage.

"LAZARUS IN BLACK"

(5:29)

1943

Word is, Skate's got it back. Where it been, baby? Ask the devil, the man can play. The week John Rose Ltd. drops its contract with Harry Lord—citing commercial irresponsibility, dismal sales, and an utter lack of musical value—Skate's stock goes up another ten points from Harlem to Bedford Stuy. And if he's bugged about not bringing in the bread the way he used to, he can console himself that he's found his tongue again, his wind and flutter and tremolo and the soul to play it through. Looking back on it, it had been so simple, an equation anyone could have written on the dust of a windowpane: more music meant less junk. He could do what he wanted without the powder; someone ought to say the same thing to Yardbird. Skate, up off his bony knees, tips back the sax like a slow drink of something longed-for and hits a ♯ he's never reached before. It may only be relief or it may be salvation. Listen.

They carry Lela out of the ladies' and a taxi is waiting for them on the street. They drape her across Harry's lap and Skate sits in front, turned round in his seat, on his knees, bending over to talk to her, saying, *Baby, baby, hang on, baby, Skate's here, baby, and Harry, too, we love you, baby, baby, don't die.*

It's the first time but not the last that he's seen tears in Harry's eyes. The man suffers for love, maybe that's where the music comes from. Tragedy's a jazz tradition: how we love them all to death, our saints. Skate, having once seen his own name written as if forever into obscurity, wishes it all over again, all his hell, if somehow Lela will pull through. Now and then Harry looks up from the singer's closed eyes to gaze at him as if asking the black angel to bring her back, bring her back. You gave it to her. You lit the candle and cooked it up. You taught her how to find a vein, to squeeze and to hold. Now bring her back.

Neon floats by on Broadway and the moon wheels high overhead. When they arrive at the hospital there are orderlies out front with a stretcher and they bear her away into a white room without shadows while Skate and Harry search pockets for matches, light each other's cigarettes, stare together through a window looking out on nothing memorable, and, after an hour's slow pacing, lean toward one another and embrace.

Word is: Skate's got it back. Himself, the want and the need to feel love. Laying his tongue to the reed, he swallows and the sound is like no other. When Lela finally gets out of the clinic, three months on a dry run back to sanity, he tells her that he sent her messenger away and there will be nothing white to dream about anymore, nothing but blood in her blood. "And, baby, that's all there's ever gonna be from now on."

Her second week out, they record "Lazarus in Black," Skate's first composition. The title is Lela's idea, though there's not much to find of it in lyrics that words can't write. Back back back here here here, etc. Heart heart want want and on through the music, Lela only follows Skate's shivers and blows, Harry deep into his left hand, giving just enough for air. It is the first recording on the Sho Nuf label, a basement-run outfit that will go out of business two years later. An anomaly title on a collection of "Lela Maar Sings Harry Lord." But Lela still sings; still. Listen.

"TIME IS ONLY BORROWED"

(3:48)

1943

A short piece, more blues than straight jazz, a throwback almost to the thirties, a different time, and Lela feels comfort in singing it. The composition may be Harry's but she's kept the lyrics, as always, to herself. From me to you, Valentine. I've written down the words for you and sung them for us both.

Valentine, calling from a phone booth, still can't reach Lela at the studio, and no one's saying where she's been. Eleven rings at her home number and a man answers, "Who is it?"

"I need to speak to Lela."

"Who is this?"

"A friend."

"Lela has no friends. Only lovers and worshipers."

"I'm both."

After a short pause during which they measure each other's breathing, Lord and Valentine hang up on each other.

Having sold the brownstone to pay off his attorney, Valentine is in need of a place to hide himself. Jack, his only remaining friend and provider, has given him an address.

"You can stay there nights only. Don't show up till after ten, and be back on the street before dawn. The place isn't being watched but there are neighbors. Knock twice, with an interval between the two."

"When do we move?"

"When the Pole lowers his asking price."

"But what if he doesn't?"

"If he doesn't? We feed him to the sharks." Jack's smile, faded from years on the run, lasts too briefly. "We could always ask your girlfriend for the money. She still good for a touch?"

"She's given enough already, Jack. All she can manage."

"Just asking." Then he adds, "You carrying anything?"

Valentine says he's clean.

Jack presses a pistol into his hand. "Hacker sends his love."

The gun fits too easily into Valentine's palm; a derringer, really, with a mother-of-pearl handle. He gives it back. "I couldn't use it."

"It's for effect, Val. In case the Pole gets funny on you."

But Valentine resists. "Tell Hacker I'll get the photos. One way or the other, but no guns."

The shadow of Woudner is between them. Ends and means. Jack touches Valentine's shoulder. "Life and death, Val. It's such a dirty business. Don't let us down."

His hosts are nearly silent when he arrives, showing him to his room, a converted pantry with a cot set up in one corner and a few shelves cleared for his things. "If the call comes when I'm out, you only have to note the time and place," he reminds them.

The man, short, balding, timid, speaks up. "Three days," he says. "You can only stay three days. That's the deal."

Valentine nods, closing the door, then sits for a long time on the cot before leaning to unlace his shoes.

The Pole is a phantom. An escaped Jew from Treblinka who has traversed Europe, across the Baltic to London and by ship to New York, carrying photographs that he claims are proof of the Final Solution. To date, there is rumor but no proof, nothing for the press to hold up as undeniable. The great Shut Up has been going on for years now. Witnesses have been discredited, or silenced, one after another, and the Pole, calling himself Jacek, is playing it cool. He avoids the police, the military, and the various Jewish agencies, preferring, he says, to deal with criminals. "I will *sell* what I have, to be sure that it will be published." Previous samples, given freely to English and American authorities, have been suppressed. The FBI is looking for him. Hacker's group, nameless and subterranean, and for which Valentine is an occasional courier, has found him first.

Valentine hasn't yet seen him. Jack has told him Jacek's story. Barbed wire, ovens, dogs, a powerful new gas, mass slavery. The stripping of fillings and wedding rings from the About to Die. The exhumation of mass graves from previous slaughters to recover the booty missed the first time around.

"So how'd he get free?" Valentine wants to know.

"With the corpses. They buried him alive but the grave was shallow. He says he dug his way upward and just walked away."

"And the photos?"

"Official Nazi files smuggled from a camp."

Valentine wonders aloud. "If he's lying . . ."

"Hacker would kill him. You know that."

Valentine will be the carrier whenever the money is made available. Jack is out touching up his Jewish contacts, those he can still trust since the warrant was put out for his arrest as well as Valentine's, Hacker's, and a dozen clandestine *others*. Sides aren't so easy to define these days: Hacker is a communist looking for an opening in the war; Jack remains anarchist to the core, unsullied by passing time and failure, now bronzed in experience and firmly on the way to a life sentence. *Incorrigible* is the word that best applies. The others are a mixture of amateur and professional: draft-dodgers, ex-cons on a political lark, a few old-line thirties radicals, myriad women believing first in their men and second in their causes. Valentine, living the lifelong waking dream of revolution, has acquired the habit of shrugging, answering neither yes nor no to the simplest of questions. Tea? Coffee? Sugar? One lump or two? Do you believe in God? In America? In justice?

In the pantry darkness, in the patch of sky above his bed, he writes his answers. Shopworn phrases from Marx, Bakunin, Lincoln, and Sarah Valentine. The point of living is in light. As versus darkness. Love, as versus murder. Whatever speaks my name, as versus loneliness.

His hosts hear laughter from the other side of the door.

"Three nights," the husband says to his wife. "Three nights and no more. I should have put my foot down this time. They take advantage of us because we don't have any children."

As versus loneliness. The last time he saw Lela was a month ago, just after he'd crashed through a third-story window, leaving his comrades to be arrested without him, their meeting place having been staked out for God knows how long, Hacker's first mistake in weeks. Running down a long alley, he'd awaited the roar of gunfire at his back, a bullet to pierce his brain, but there'd been only his shoes on the rainy pavement and the beating of his heart. The enterprise had seemed, just for a moment, ridiculous; mortality putting the screws to idealism. Lela had taken his call at the studio and had answered in a code they'd worked out long since, then had met him three hours later in a hotel in Brooklyn, far from the trail of his bleeding and broken glass. She'd sweated and shivered in his arms for a few hours, her eyes on the wind-up clock next to the bed. By this time he knew it wasn't Harry she was worried about but her shot. He'd caught her at a bad hour and his love was crowded out by another kind of worship. They hadn't made love, though there'd been time enough. Naked and intertwined, they'd lain awake, looking over each other's shoulders, he toward the door and she toward the window. That existential waiting for the scene just to end.

And now his calls go unanswered, just as his gestures have come to lose their meaning. When not hiding in places like this and waiting for late-night calls from Hacker, he wanders the stony length of Manhattan, uncertain which door to enter and which to pass by. Once a revolutionary, he has been reduced to a thief. Hacker sends him to army recruitment centers, post offices, precincts, and various apartments for documents, letters, files, photographs; evidence of conspiracy, crimes against humanity, recorded trespasses of liberty, blueprints for the American machine. He no longer bothers to read what he steals or to write in his own journal of the revolution. There is no revolution other than words crawling over words.

Cause or effect? Living on Lela's money and saying it's for the Movement. Because I've failed I live on her money? Or because I live on her money I've failed? One hand is constantly washing the other of guilt.

He persists, his skill as a thief surprising and confusing him. A master of bolt locks, seams of windows, back stairways, and rooftops, he has learned to walk invisibly among his fellow men, his footsteps soundless, his coming and going (his short-term history) unknown. Only Hacker knows where to find him, and now and then Jack has his address. A few times he has seen others in the network, while passing parcels to them under coffee-shop tables or through library shelves, one hand reaching for a book and the other for stolen letters. How will I recognize him? He will be wearing a hat and will have an umbrella hanging from his left wrist. He will be carrying a handful of flowers in his right hand and a newspaper in his left. She will be in the third row, third seat from the right. At the end of the first act she will stand and move to the row behind yours. You will leave the package under your seat.

A man with blue eyes, a woman with a green silk scarf. A fake limp, a mustache pasted over his lip. Mismatched shoes, horn-rimmed glasses.

No one has a name.

Lying on his cot, Valentine cannot sleep. Dreamless, he lets his thoughts drift from Lela to Hacker to the war to the past. When this war ends he will begin again, a new organization, a plan, a manifesto. He will revive his old vocabulary and learn again to put a name to things he believes in. He falls asleep just as the phone rings once, then silence, then a second ring. Them. His host is at the door before he can tie his shoes, giving him an address on the West Side, a hotel. "Room 411. Five-fifteen exactly. Don't knock, the door will open for you."

The front lobby of the Gideon Arms is empty and Valentine silently climbs the stairs to the fourth floor, stopping at each landing to gaze down a carpeted hallway lined with closed doors. He is a few minutes late, having badly timed his walk up West End Avenue, and when he arrives at the door marked 411 he is strangely out of breath, his nerves worn thin from a brief meeting with Jack near Times Square. Handing him an envelope, Jack had said to be careful. "No one's ever seen this Jacek except Hacker, and this isn't your kind of job."

"What should I be frightened of? The law?"

"No," Jack had answered. "Of treachery."

The door is open and he pushes it forward, then slips into darkness. "Are you alone?" a voice asks him.

"As always," he answers. The blow comes from behind, hard but yielding. He sleeps a black sleep and awakens in a car, Hacker with him in the back seat, his boss holding a pistol with both hands.

Valentine says, "Explain."

Hacker tells him, "Confess."

"To what crime?"

"The others were arrested and not you."

"I was next to the window. I jumped and ran."

Hacker says only, "We'll see."

For two months Valentine is kept in the basement of a warehouse somewhere in New Jersey. He is fed and interrogated at regular intervals. The accusation is the same: his freedom is a crime against the imprisoned. There is no trial, there are only questions, including his own. "What about Jacek?"

"There is no Jacek. He was my fiction."

"No photographs, then?"

"We set you up, Val. To see if you'd tip the police."

"I don't know any police."

"Then what about this?" Hacker produces a book with various numbers written on the back page. His and Lela's code, each number meaning an address, a day of the week, a time of day or night. For the past year they have kept a calendar of trysts written in code to fool Harry or whoever might, like Hacker, catch on to them.

"There's a woman," Valentine says. "She's married. We use a code to remember our rendezvous."

Hacker copies out one of the sets of numbers. "What's this mean?"

"A hotel on York Avenue. Room 310, October 14 at nine o'clock."

"And this one?"

"Same place a week later."

"And was she there?"

"No. I haven't seen her in over a month."

"Why not?"

Valentine says he doesn't know.

Hacker wants to know her name but Valentine refuses to tell him.

"Why not? Her husband might tell us where she is. If she corroborates your story, you're free."

"And if not?"

Instead of answering, Hacker asks him to decode the next half-dozen meeting places and times, and for the next few weeks Jack is sent to keep an eye out, but Lela never arrives. Nothing else is brought against Valentine but Hacker insists on keeping him locked up. "We have to be cautious, Val. You understand our position. Didn't you do a stretch in prison once?"

"Nine years."

"Jack told me. That Woudner business. You'd have done better to join the Party."

Valentine shakes his head. "Communists. I have trouble shaking hands with you. I always want to count my fingers afterward."

On the last date in the notebook, Jack finds Lela. Bringing his news to the warehouse, he confirms to Hacker that the woman is Lela Maar. Jack asks Valentine, "Why didn't you tell me it was Lela? I could have helped you out." She had waited for more than an hour in the hotel room before giving up and going out to the street to hail a taxi.

"How did she look?"

"Not bad. A bit on the thin side. I'm sorry about all this, Val. Hacker's losing his grip and I should have trusted you."

All the same, he is cast adrift. The organization has no more use for him; his identity is compromised and his anger suspect. He has kept a secret lover in his background and can no longer be trusted. They give him a half-filled suitcase of old clothes and twenty dollars, drive him to Battery Park, and leave him standing on the sidewalk.

A few days later he is reunited with Lela. In an Upper West Side hotel, she tells him about her stay in the clinic, her cure. "The pain, Val. All the pain I'd been storing up for years was there. I felt like an animal and I lived like one. They put me in a padded cell and bound my arms."

They comfort each other through a long evening, then work out a new series of codes, one day here and the next day somewhere else, varying the dates and hours according to Lela's work schedule. Valentine tells her his work is ended but she reminds him she has enough money for both of them. "I'll be working again soon. I can help you. We can both start over."

Valentine says he won't. It's finished for him, he tells her.

"For you it's never finished. Are you writing?"

"Page after page, all of them blank."

"Your time will come, Val."

"It's come and gone."

The day she records "Time Is Only Borrowed," he is there. Dressed as a janitor, his uniform stolen from a nearby closet, he stands in the back of a white-paneled room and listens carefully for the lyrics, but the drone of a fan overhead cuts the words into fragments, solitary syllables of time spent, time wasted, time wanted, time denied. Then he returns the janitor's uniform to its hanger in a dark corner, takes a stairway down to the back door, and steps out into the street, where the wind is blowing a riff he's always heard but never before listened to.

"LIE DOWN ON THE NUMBER"

(6:14)

1943

They told me she was clean and maybe for a while she was. Junkies is sometimes secreter than spies and everybody's got something up their sleeve, a gun or the king a spades or a needle track a yard long. She was married to Harry but he must have never seen her in the light or he'd a done something more than he ever did about stopping her. He was never an easy man to read, Harry Lord. All these little silences used to build up in him like he was hurtin the same as Lela. Maybe because she was unfaithful most of the time, or maybe he was just given to storms and rages and all that because that's where his sounds come from. You ever listen to "Lie Down on the Number"? Just about the maddest jazz I ever heard back when we was all doing sensual stuff. Mad, mad. Not like crazy, though it sounded that, too. I mean rip-roaring pissed off, that left hand of Harry's like a fist coming down, and Skate's riffs chasing him up, trying to get his right hand back into it to soften things a bit. You listen real close and you'll hear Lela trying to figure out where to go, running and hiding from Harry's piano while Skate's like some whole crowd of frantic angels trying to hang on to her. Real fast stuff and you only had to listen to it once or twice to get the idea that Lela was already back on the horse, like how her voice trails off at the end of these long breathy phrases, just goes off into nowhere like that, dot dot dot, and then not a sound for a real long time . . .

"PROFUSION"

(8:15)

1943

Lela spreads her legs like wings and is entered by a man, men. Fanatic with want, they spin a pollen that drifts through a windless chamber in search of her womb. A sigh escapes her, a gasp, and we call it lyrics. The melody of more and more and deep and more. The percussion, perhaps, of an orgasm.

When is the mystery. When was the page turned, the womb wetted? Go ask God when His will was done.

Harry, in surprise, holds her for long minutes in his arms, telling her she must not leave him. "Where will you go? Whose music will you sing?"

Valentine smooths away a lock of hair wet with perspiration along her forehead. "I regret everything," he tells her, "but the life I've lived with you."

She gives herself to a nameless man in an overcoat. They find a doorway on a side street and step in from under the rain. "You're Lela Maar," he says, and she says to him, "You're anyone."

Jo Jo is holding her needle but wants a lay before she nods out. The saints go marching in. No one says no and the nodding is perpetual. Winter light fills a bare room and she books passage for Europe, where there's said to be a place for women like her, a treatment for the junk that won't leave scars. Fingers forgets the date, November or December, maybe even later. It was a cold day, he says. After Thanksgiving, maybe. I don't know and I didn't keep no diary neither. According to legend, we imagine Lela Maar on her own on a ship to a foreign land, kissing soft goodbyes into her palm and blowing them across the bay to New York, to Valentine, to Harry and to Skate, to the sound of a song once recorded and never ending, and to you who sit breathing over these words, believing every one of them. She disappears.

IN WHICH PAGE PEDDLES DIRTY POSTCARDS

The trick to self-defense is not to get shrill about it, to say what you have to say and let that stand. Still, they want the words—the story behind the picture, so to speak—simple captions for the visually impaired. And because I've lived the better part of a decade plus in various arenas of mayhem, one story just naturally leads to another. But here's the hitch: human memory fails me. It is too frail and viscous and pliant, and I have a tendency, in the retelling, to ramble. All I have as solid evidence are the photographs themselves, and I can paw through them as often as I like, gradually wearing away the chemicals to reveal patches of dying light underneath. I can piece together my past into something of a chronology, annals and passages to be examined and unraveled. I said *unraveled*, you notice. I never said *solved*, as in Mr. Mustard in the study with a wrench.

I'm begging for an alibi, I know. And I know that even Jane's love won't get me off the hook. Not just yet. I never deny that it was me who took the pictures but I'm forever reminding the world that I'm not in them. For anyone but Jane that's somehow too fine a line to draw.

I read that my mother had a habit of lighting matches and letting them burn like fuses to her fingers. Her own way of tempting fate, of putting God to the test: Burn me and I'll know I've been forsaken. It's been the same for me, taking snapshots of the war, like lighting little fires and hoping like hell the house won't burn to the ground. The smell of sulphur inspired me to take unholy risks with my soul. I was snapping those pictures because I *believed* what I was seeing, the murder of men and women before my very eyes. And when I survived every contact, I assumed there was some reason for it: to take *more* pictures, have another whiff of sulphur.

So here's my alibi. I let the flame decide. And it wasn't until I loved Jane and she persisted in loving me, until I was back from it all with a mirror in my forehead, standing over Hunter's crib and reaching to take him into my arms, that the matchstick ran out on me and I felt the surprise, and relief, of its burning.

1
ALGIERS
1961

I awakened in a dusty darkness, the ripples of a headache moving outward and down to my eyes. The tea, hemlock, elixir of finite death. Lakhdar, my friend and drug-dealer, had slipped me a mickey, and in the windowless room where they'd locked me I had no way of knowing if it was day or night. The heat was the same as before, leaving a weight in my chest. In what seemed like many hours I had seen no one and heard nothing. Reaching around the floor on which I lay, I could feel only stone. My camera and bag had been taken from me and my pockets emptied. All they'd left me was a pack of cigarettes and two matches.

I'd been in Algeria for a week, and every day there had been bodies. They seemed to spring up from beneath the cobblestones; some were removed faster than others, tagged, mourned over, buried or burned or shipped overseas for last rites. Once, while walking through the European sector, I thought I'd escaped the horror until I came upon a quiet street shaded with palms, houses hidden behind sandy walls and iron gates, and there, lying in a shallow gutter, a shoeless foot awaited me. Eating alone in the restaurant that night, I picked warily through a plate of spaghetti, half expecting to find a finger or an eyeball, a testicle, a toe, any piece of man or woman. Drinking wine, I tasted blood. That's when I should have made a run for it.

Lakhdar picked me up on the tourist beat, the hotel-guide routine. "This way to hashish, American boy." Fingering my camera and asking if I took good pictures. Two days running we'd taken to the street, from the Casbah to the Esplanade and up to Bab el Oued, the poor European section where the Spaniards and Italians and Maltese hung out in droves, tongues hanging from so much street warfare. Ever the tourist, I'd snapped a few pictures, telling myself it was for Isabelle, to show her what she'd missed. The hash I'd bought from Lakhdar had been first-rate, head-turning stuff, making my vision pointillist and dispersed, and mingling with the heat to send me heavenward. Lakhdar, in the role of boy-guide, asked me questions.

"You look for girls?"

"Me? I'm only a tourist."

"But this is a war."

And me saying stupidly, "Excitement, fun. Lead me there."

So Lakhdar did, spiking my mint tea with Allah knows what, and in the darkness of my cell I wanted to know why.

I rubbed my temples and waited for the pain in my head to subside. When I felt up to it I lit a cigarette, letting the match burn down to my fingers. The light upon my hands reminded me that I was there and had not gone pffft into some desert cosmos, hashished into oblivion. The cigarette was comforting though the tobacco was harsh on my dry throat. I smoked it in short drags, slowly, happy for the orange glow in the blackness, and when it had burned to the end I lit another with the remaining ember. Anything to pierce that darkness.

When the pack was empty, the room was immeasurably darker and more frightening. A reminder of blindness: eyes opened or closed, there was no difference. I slept and I awakened and the heat seemed to have lessened. The sweat was dry on my forearms and my head was cool. Reaching around the room, I touched the crust of a heel of bread and, farther on, a bottle of water. Bread and water, that's how it was. I took a long drink from the bottle and suddenly felt an urge to pee. After a long moment of thinking it over, I stood and walked with arms outstretched, searching for the farthest corner of the room, then relieved myself against the wall. On hands and knees, I found my way back to the patch of rags that made up my bed. I broke the bread into small pieces, softening it with my fingers before putting it into my mouth, chewing, and swallowing it down.

"This war is nearly ended. All that is left is random dying and continual wordcraft in Paris and Evian and New York. We have won. This is the first thing that you must understand. The ultras go on killing but they know they are lost. In another year there will not remain a single living European on the face of Algeria."

Mostefa speaking, the leader of the *katiba*, my captor. Before the sortie, he offered me bread, dried lamb, some cold potatoes. He was not an Arab, he said, but a Kabyle. "From the mountains."

Accepting the food, I asked him when I might expect to be set free.

He gestured toward the doorway. "Stand up and walk away. Where will you go? Which way is your hotel? Your country? Would you walk alone during the night through the streets of the Casbah?"

I knew better than to ask for an escort.

"You are here for your eyes," Mostefa told me. "And when you, and that," gesturing to my camera, "have seen enough, you will be liberated."

It was not so unlike any other night on the town. Mostefa's boys dressed perhaps more carefully than usual, checking their pouches for ammunition. They were silent but filled with the anticipation of encounter. Eyes guarded, words spent only to soothe frayed nerves.

How do I look, Abdul?

Like a million bucks, Lakhdar.

Mostefa pulled a *djellaba* over my head to hide the dangling camera, then taught me how to extract it from the long folds, through a slit at just about hip level, the same slit that allowed the men of the *faoudj* to pull out their guns in the space of seconds. Lakhdar extinguished the lamps and we climbed a stone stairway to the outside. For a brief moment I looked upward, seeing enormous stars strewn against a moonless black sky, and I felt a primal awe, a sense of blessing. The men around me, weapons hidden from view, seemed almost holy to me. I forgot about the throat-slitting. Across from us were stacked houses, and farther on a wall bordering a garden. There were five of us: Mostefa, Lakhdar, and two others of the *faoudj* whom I'd never seen before. My trembling self. Each of them was carrying a pistol, a long knife, and a single grenade. Besides my camera, I toted two rolls of film and a packet of flashes, but all I really wanted was a cigarette. Mostefa led us down the street, and within a few dozen yards we fanned out and dispersed into various distances so as not to appear together.

Coming to a narrow square, we melded into a crowd and crossed slowly toward the other side. A police van was parked in the middle of the square and three French policemen, sweating in their kepis, searched passing faces. Lakhdar was the first to arrive at the other side of the square, and he disappeared into an alley. I looked decidedly un-Arab despite the *djellaba* and felt watched as I cruised toward the perimeter of the police van. Imminence, I was thinking. Imminence and omen. One of the *djoundi* had to be watching me, and the police van was still a half-dozen yards away. The menace nearly undid the movement of my legs. I concentrated on vision, the fruit in a nearby stall, bruised apples and overripe oranges, putting fear to either side of me. The weight of my camera seemed magnified ten times and it slapped against my belly with every step. Moving more swiftly, I came to the street at the end of the square, the *djoundi*'s breath now heavy at my back, and Mostefa, emerging from the alley, greeted me with a thin smile.

"You didn't see the policemen?"

I answered that of course I'd seen them.

"You might have saved yourself."

"Your man was at my back."

Mostefa said no, there was no man.

"What about him?" When I turned around there was no one there. We were alone in the alley.

That's when he knew he had me. Fear would be my watchdog from now on. Watchdog or sheepdog, barking at me if I strayed.

Then Mostefa said we should hurry and, without asking where to, I followed. He led me up the alley and into a shop where we were greeted by a girl of about sixteen, close to my tender age. She and Mostefa exchanged a few words of Arabic; then she turned and showed us to the back of the shop, out another door, into yet another alley (though they were, in fact, streets, they would always seem to me to be alleys: gutterless straits of dust and dogshit with crooked windows overlooking them), and when we had crossed to the other side and slipped down a short stairway into a cellar, I heard the first explosions. There were two of them right away and the third after an interval of seconds. "Your policemen," Mostefa said. Next we heard gunfire, a few bursts of an automatic answered by pistol shots.

"How?"

"Lakhdar is very accurate with a thrown grenade."

We remained hidden for a long time, hearing occasional footsteps outside, and sometimes a passing motorbike. The alley was too narrow for cars. We were two blocks away from the square, yet I could clearly hear the screaming of women, more gunfire, and all I could think of doing was stripping the *djellaba* from my body. Lifting it away, I could smell myself and I was nearly sick from it. Mostefa, too, listened to the mayhem in the streets but his eyes were blank and impassive. Only when the streets had become quiet for some time did he stand, signal me to follow, and lead me back.

When we arrived at the square, I saw the aftermath of a *ratonnade*, a rat hunt. After the grenades had fallen, a squadron of police had descended into the square to maintain order and had been attacked by stone-throwing women chanting *You-you-you*. Though the police had held themselves in check, the OAS had not. A band of ultras, once associated with that slapstick mobster Jo Ortiz, had ridden into the square on motorbikes and sprayed the women with gunfire. Pursued by the FLN, the ultras had escaped into the Bab el Oued district and dispersed. This was the story as it would be written, as though it all had been so clear, the armies and their movements so sharply defined. Yet the actual *ratonnade*—mobs of *pieds noirs* storming into the Casbah with clubs, pistols, chains, and knives—could not possibly be interpreted as the maneuver of an army. Windows had been broken and cars burned and two were killed, it was written, less than had been taken out by Lakhdar's simple grenade. By the time I arrived with Mostefa, the square was littered with bodies, some moving a wounded arm or leg or simply rocking in pain, a few others not moving at all. Mostefa held my arm and led me through the carnage until we came upon the body of a woman face down in the dirt. "Now, Page. Now your camera."

I reached through the slit in my robe and unhooked the Nikon from its chain while Mostefa bent to roll the woman over. Distance = 6′. Speed = 124. I set a sharp focus, passing the lens over the reddish-brown stain above her belly, to her face contorted in pain. "She's not dead," I said.

Mostefa answered, "But she will be. Save her, Page. Now. With your camera."

The woman lifted and dropped her hips, shifting her torso in pain, and when she turned her head from side to side I could no longer keep her within the rectangle of my lens. Mostefa was urging me to go ahead, shoot, and it was then that I realized that the whole thing had been staged for just this moment, choreographed by Mostefa, the grenades having been intended only to incite a *ratonnade*, the rain of bullets certain to catch somewhere in the vicinity of an innocent heart. This woman writhing in the dust was about to become a postcard for the political wing of the FLN. *See them murdering us. See how our women die under their Western guns.* A wider lens might have captured the torn bodies of the French policemen; a wider angle still would have encompassed the entire square, that bazaar of agony.

I focused on the woman, who thrashed her head from side to side. Blood now covered her chest and shoulders, and when she held her head still, looking through wet eyes toward the black box poised above her, I dropped the shutter, a blink in time, and she was dead.

For the next half-hour, Mostefa led me by the arm, from corpse to wounded, instructing me as to the angle and number of shots to make. An earless boy grinned into the lens, a trace of blood running down his neck. An old man lay beneath a weary palm tree, both hands held over his sightless eyes, the blood already dried between his fingers.

I changed to a new roll of film, aimed, fired.

Bodies were loaded into the back of a truck destined for the hospital and I lifted myself onto the tailgate, adjusting the lens to a wider image, a group portrait this time. Afterward, I was sick all over my shoes, and when that didn't make things any better, I stood up straight and aimed the camera at Mostefa like a pistol. Though he had a pistol of his own, I did all the shooting, one, two, three, stealing his soul from him in onionskin layers, but he wouldn't fall dead, he just stood there without any expression, waiting for me to run out of film.

You felt the burning coming from somewhere near your throat and when you opened your mouth to exhale you were surprised not to see a ball of flame or even a trace of smoke, as from the barrel of a rifle. Lying on a hard floor, you awakened to the roar of your own heartbeat, a railroad sound, rhythmic and incessant, and you were still there and they were sleeping all around you with their pistols in their hands, and someone in a brown robe was standing sentry at the doorway, his eyes roaming over the tops of heads to rest upon yours, unblinking. Pillowing your hands under your head, you closed your eyes and pretended again to sleep, but under your lids was the unreeling cinema, a flip flip flip of postcards of bone, flesh, teeth, hair, eyeballs exposed to the sunlight, pupils receding, the shadow of a passing black dog covering this woman's face, a trace of red spittle on that man's lips, you could have sworn he said your name in dying. You are a spectator now. Or, worse, a voyeur.

Or, worse still, a journalist. Or, at black bottom, a photohistorian. *Death from Life* for every caption.

And then you slept, sometime after dawn, a dreamless and satisfying sleep that lasted only minutes. And then they were shaking you awake again and saying, "Go, go up," and you rose on aching feet, breathing hard as if after a long run up the stairway, and followed them into an alley, down a stairway, through a window, to some other address—safe, they tell you—another place to hide, and they lead you to a corner covered in rags and tell you "Sleep," but the sun has risen and will not set again for many hours, so that even with your eyes tightly closed, even with your forearm shielding them from the light, there is that reddish tinge below your eyelids, fanning the sparks of a headache that refuses to go away.

We were in the mountains and an old man squatted across from me to sharpen his knife against a flat stone. I thought that there might be a picture in it somewhere, the long shadows framing the man just so, his back slightly turned to me as the sun set behind me. When his knife was sufficiently sharpened, he rose from his haunches to search out a goat he had left tethered nearby. Straddling the goat's back, he hooked an arm under its lower jaw, yanked the head upward, and with his other hand passed the knife cleanly across the throat.

"We indeed created man," reads the Koran, "and we know what his soul whispers within him, and we are nearer to him than the jugular vein."

The goat bucked once, its knees descending, and when the man released its head it fell like a stone to the ground. Bending low, he raised the goat by the hind legs, bound them, and hung the feet high on a pointed pole. Blood ran freely from the goat's severed neck to a flat rock underneath.

I reached under my *djellaba*, took out my camera, and set the distance to twelve feet. Seeing the black box, the old man turned away his eyes, but before I could focus and fire Lakhdar knocked the Nikon from my hands.

"He is afraid for his soul," the boy explained.

"That makes two of us."

This, O Lord, is an alley off the rue Somewhere where the ultras cornered a pair of stray *djoundi* and did them in with a few quick bursts of their automatics. The night's mascara, showing blue in this photo (at the throat, the eyes, the severed hands), would be revealed as scarlet in the light of day.

This, old man, is a street in Bab el Oued where a series of *stroungas* took out the fruitstand beneath which was a hideout, once, for yours truly. We arrived too late to see the corpses, but I'm told there were three. I took this photo after the fact and all you can see is the spoiled fruit. Forgive me the poor focus as well as the weak metaphor; we were in our usual mortal hurry.

Here is a burning car, ordinary, the shade of the smoke giving evidence of something human trapped inside. Someone from the prefecture, Mostefa told me, and although I seldom took pictures of his victories, even Mostefa liked the *allure* of this one, his sense of symbolism finally pierced. He tacked it up on the basement wall one day and all the men of the *faoudj* trooped by to admire it.

A hand, a face, a series of bullet holes random as Pollock's brush splatters (which is to say, not *entirely* random). Here, a double negative I developed myself, a man-man who was dead-dead in the daylight over daylight because he happened to be standing in the street just then. We had come up from a hole in the earth, having hidden for many days there, hunted and hungry, Mostefa gone away somewhere, to the Wilaya, to his heaven, we didn't know. Without sunlight, without words. We ate bits of hard bread, gritty *semoule*, sometimes a sliver of dried lamb tasting mostly of salt. Perhaps we were eating stone and didn't know the difference. It was another cellar and the air was as old as the city. When I wept from fear or from loneliness, Abdul ben Kezra cuffed me with his hairy fist. I learned to weep silently, swallowing my sobs, sleeping and then waking without knowing I had slept. Seated or reclining on a cool layer of dust, stone beneath me, stone to either side of me. I avoided thoughts of the void, the beyond, anything that might drive me crazy. Lakhdar, who was still with us, found a few bent cigarettes, God knows where, which I smoked hungrily, one or two breaths at a time, and then extinguished with my fingers, saving them, hoarding that smoke. It was all that kept me from weeping aloud and being bruised by ben Kezra.

Some of us were dead. I could hear the others hauling corpses to far corners and saying prayers over them, their wounds become anecdotal and beside the point, their souls given up to Allah, and the food rationed more freely among the still-living. It was Mostefa, ever an archangel, who came for us, lifting up the trap door and letting in a blinding and awful sunlight to show us to each other: each of us standing in an opposite corner, our piles of shit hoarded against various walls, faces stained and creased with days of darkness. When I was again above ground, Mostefa handed me my camera. He had carried it through skirmishes and confused battles as though it were some religious ornament. The body of a Frenchman lay at his feet.

Life after death. I struck a match and an ill wind extinguished it at once. I hung the camera round my neck, lifted it to my open eye, and took this picture.

2 DAO SANCTUARY MISSION, TAY NINH PROVINCE 1966

As a joke, or a symbolic gesture, I began wearing an empty holster, sometimes putting a banana or a book where the firearm should have been. Six months in Vietnam hadn't steamed the sass out of me yet, and even though I was older than most of the fighting men and had seen more war than many, I hadn't yet participated; so my gesture was oddly fearsome. I was that *asshole walkin naked in a war zone,* and a colonel up at Cam Ranh Bay tried to fill that holster with his own Colt, telling me, "Death is no breeze, son. Why not face it with some heat in your pocket?"

This is what that empty holster meant to them: that I was marked for a body bag. And in their superstition of anything marked, they avoided me like the plague. I was worse than contact because I was among them, even behind the dotted lines.

After selling a dozen pages to Time/Life, I took the cash and moved out of harm's way, to a mountain retreat in the Tay Ninh Province. There were Catholics there, Buddhists, Tao sitters, and a number of orphans, all living together in a converted mission that was by this time neither a hospital nor a hotel. The director was an Australian ex-priest named Dorn who'd been there for fifteen years and who had walked a zigzag path from Jesus Christ to Florence Nightingale and, by the time I showed up in his camp, had long since gone silent on both religion and healing. I suppose he was just waiting for the war to arrive and put a bullet to his dream. In the meantime, he ruminated, sitting lotus on his back porch and watching the fruit rot in the trees. When I arrived and introduced myself, saying Spec 4 Carson had sent me, he just glanced at my empty holster, nodded, and told me to go into the courtyard and eat. Not everyone was allowed such easy entry and I've always assumed it was the holster that did it. One crazy recognizing another.

There were a dozen other Americans there before me, two of them deserters, a navy nurse named Gilliam, some journalists, and a group from Recon who'd come up to make maps. The mountains were VC shelter but the whole province was pacified for the time being. Occasionally there was a murder or a kidnapping, someone's head showing up in the soup, but on the whole it was no more dangerous than southern California and you could pretend, most of the time, that you were really somewhere else.

Gilliam was the first round-eye female I'd gotten close to in months. The only women I'd had had been stand-ups in Saigon—*bestfucks*, as they called themselves. "Hey you, hieu! Best fuck?" Gilliam had that starved look and the eyes of Bernadette. She'd come to save the world and had something sacred under her skirt. Me and my empty holster didn't have what she was looking for.

Her first words to me were, "What's *your* story?"

I told her I was a photographer.

"Killed any Cong?"

"No."

"Then what'd you come for? To sniff the dead?"

She had me there. I took that crack of hers higher up into the mountains for a long walk-through, lit up a fat stick, and tried to ascend into the clouds, Page's Assumption, but when I felt myself still on terra firma there seemed nothing to do but weep. I tried it but couldn't. I hadn't yet cried in Vietnam, even when I'd seen American dead. In Algeria they'd all been Arab or French or Italian, human but not of my tribe. I had thought that seeing dead Americans would move me to tears, but no. That would have been a luxury. I'd cried in Algiers and never since. Whatever came out of my eyes was more like sand than water. So on the mountain I just told everyone to go to hell, figuring that way I'd at least have company. You, too, Gilliam. And I stomped back down the path to the mission.

Rawlings, one of the deserters, wanted to see my pictures. We were sharing a bowl of rice mixed with corned beef and passing a bottle of Jack Daniel's in the courtyard. Rawlings was nineteen and thought he'd get his ass to Sweden as soon as he could find a boat out.

I reminded him he was in the mountains. "No boats here, Rawlings."

"I meant from somewhere else."

"You got any contacts? Someone to help?"

He told me not to worry. "I been here a year. I know my way around."

Looking over my prints, he said I had a lousy focus. "This one here is so damn fuzzy. What happened?"

I told him that sometimes I was shooting on the run, one-handed. Now and then there wasn't time to switch the distance. Sometimes it was nerves.

"You ought a carry a tripod."

"Thanks, Rawlings. I'll think it over."

Before coming to Nam, I'd had a few domestic assignments. The first was in Miami, doing pictures for a journalist who had interviewed a group of Cuban freedom fighters. Their eyes had seemed so hot, where those Algerian eyes had been cold. Killers wear a different gaze according to their climate. After receiving my first set of pictures from Vietnam, my agent said, "I get the impression you didn't even look through the lens. The frame always comes out like something you didn't want to see—as if you tried too late to look the other way."

I wrote that down and it became my style. Rawlings thought it was pretty shoddy but I told him I still managed to sell some things.

"But you don't fight?"

"No. I don't fight."

"That's cool," he decided. "I guess that's cool."

Later in the day he came to my cell to say how do. "You want some scag?" he asked.

I told him I was clean.

"There's a medic here with a batch of fresh needles if you're interested."

It would have been pointless to tell him I was born a junkie. That Lela had cleaned up her act too late and that junkie mothers pass on their addictions to their children. Her blood had been mine and my first shoot-up had been shortly after conception. I sensed I couldn't tell him that. He would have thought it was cool.

"Anything else?" he wanted to know. "I got a little speed with me but no grass. Acid's down the hill a ways, I could give you directions."

I told him I wanted a woman and that Gilliam would do just fine.

"That tight bitch? She's saving it up for a real rainy day. Anyway, you don't look at all like her type. She wants a *patriot*. I'd stick to the natives."

When I said something about fornicating with the red, white, and blue, he just answered, "Black and blue, Page. Ebony black and midnight blue. Those are my colors from here on in."

Each day at the mission began with Dawn Gestures, Dorn leading his followers into a glen where the exercises began, individual balancing acts invented by Dorn himself, derivative of every Asian discipline he'd ever practiced. I went along with them because there was beauty in the silence of fifty people moving among each other, arms extended, hands depicting birds, right leg uplifted and held in place, a swan settling into a crouch of flower bud, and the flower bud opening slowly to become a tree, a tiger, a dragon. The orphans were naturals; this was their recess and they moved so well together that I assumed they were following some music that I in my Western stupor couldn't hear. Dorn was usually among them, doing his own gestures with closed eyes, becoming voluntarily blind from dawn to noon and never needing so much as a guiding hand to lead him across the glen and back again. At the time I wrote it down to insanity. I was unable to believe in sanctity, though I suppose I should have been more aware of Dorn's kindnesses, the unconscious generosity in him that attracted the worst mountain killers to his mission and kept the VC from doing him in, even though he was harboring round-eye deserters and Recon and demented punk photojournalists like myself. Crazy people aren't kind the way Dorn was. They're just out of order.

In the afternoons we all went about our personal affairs while Dorn and the orphans and some adults tended the fields around the mission. This was communism such as the first Asian wrote it up: no central committees, no soviet, and no dogma, just a silent father figure with his back bent to the mud like everyone else and not an M-16 or an AK-47 in sight. Even the boys from Recon pitched in, and after a few days of sitting in my cell and sulking about my lot in life I felt sufficient shame and boredom to get up and join them. Seeing me in the field, Dorn came over and ran a finger across my sweating forehead. He tasted my sweat and said, "Jack Daniel's." Each day thereafter he repeated the ritual and on the fifth day he smiled and said, "*Dao.*"

At night, after a communal dinner of rice and steamed vegetables, the talk would begin. Smith and Carter, from Recon, were heavy readers, having toted along Spinoza and Coleridge and Baudelaire. Their conversations frightened me more than the NVA and I stayed away from them, hanging mostly with Rawlings or with Dorn or with another of the Recon group named Wright.

Wright was an astrology freak and was always asking everyone what their sign was. "I'm a Virgo with Pisces rising."

"A Sagittarian with Virgo rising."

Rawlings said he was a motherfucker with heroin rising, and nobody laughed but me.

Everyone had countless action stories about *what they'd seen*. It was inevitable over there. Put two grunts together and in no time they were comparing death scenes. I wasn't any different from them but I had pictures. Though, now that I think of it, so did they. Pictures of Mom & Pop, their dogs, their girls from back home, best friends (those high-school pictures with slicked-down hair and acne airbrushed into oblivion), their cars, their baseball teams, the gang. Rawlings had a picture of his bedroom that he said was for his good moods. "When I need one, I look at it." He was headed for that bedroom, he said, out of *this place*. The picture showed a bed and dresser, a U of Kansas pennant on the wall next to a day-glo poster of the Rolling Stones, a window looking into sunlight, and a bookshelf lined with model airplanes, comic books, a baseball glove. "When I look at this picture," he said, "I'm *there*. Take a picture that'll do the same to me, Page, and I'll buy it off you."

But I didn't take any pictures at the mission. I had come for the quiet of the place and not because of any assignment. Some clippings were sent to me while I was there and I was amazed to read the criticism of my work, a pointless nattering about my filters and my angles and my *encadrage* and very little about my subjects. It was as though I'd been snapping away at nudes, shadows, or bowls of fruit. Someone even wrote that I had an extraordinary bent and at first I read that I *was* extraordinarily bent. This was long before I lost my agency credentials and had to get a press pass through a skin magazine in London.

When Gilliam first asked to see my pictures I had the momentary illusion that I was getting somewhere with her. Pointing out an aerial view of Danang, I told her that it had been printed in *Life*, which was a lie.

She was unimpressed. "They must love you in Hanoi for providing them with air recon." Then she singled out a picture of a wounded child and asked me when I'd taken it.

"Two weeks ago, up north." I started to tell her about the firefight just below the DMZ, but she didn't want to hear about it.

"This little boy," she said. "Did you get his name?"

I said I hadn't thought of it.

"Did you give him anything? Candy? Cigarettes? A slug of whisky?"

"I just took his picture."

"You just took his picture." Her eyes hardened but all I could look at was the barest gap in her blouse, a breath of lace showing through. "When you take their pictures, Page, give them something in return. Write down their names. Faces need names, whether they're dying or not. Don't be such a parasite and don't call this place Disneyland like the others. Do that for me, Page. Don't be just another grunt with a cheap Instamatic. Try not to turn it all into some dirty cartoon."

People were coming and going like at a health spa. Civilians, Viet Cong, the recently orphaned, and now and then a few Marines with hell all over their faces. The mission was getting to be known as the place where the war wasn't, and for a while that summer there were too many hands in the fields and at night the common bowls were emptying faster than ever. If Dorn was concerned, he didn't show it. His prenoon blindness was intact and he never failed to taste my sweat in the fields each morning, as though he sensed that it was the only ritual that had any meaning for me. Maybe it meant that, Zen or not, I was converted, even if I felt in my heart I was only hedging my immortality bets. I continued to wear my gunless holster, filling it now and then with a hammer or a hand rake or a clutch of wildflowers.

Smith and Carter disappeared and were replaced by a half-dozen advisers from MACV who spent their mornings tramping around the mountain, obviously looking for something they didn't want anyone to know about. They were the only people I ever saw Dorn ask to leave, but they just waved some papers in front of his eyes as if to say, Like fun, and went off to their cells to collate their reports. Anyone who left the mission was fair game, given the concentration of VC in the area, and I made certain that at night I was well within the walls, even to the point of turning down an offer to go on recon with the MACV advisers.

"The country *looks* peaceful," one of them said. "But I can tell you it's gonna get hot here real soon. You know this guy Dorn?"

"A little."

"He VC or what?"

I said I'd heard he was Australian.

"That's not what I meant."

But I knew well enough what he meant and took a warning to Dorn. "They're here for more than recon."

Dorn just waved a hand as if to thank me for the preciously useless information. "They'll be leaving soon," he said. "Like Rawlings."

Rawlings had disappeared three days before. It wasn't the first time. I supposed he was out looking for that boat of his.

Dorn wanted to know why I hadn't taken any pictures and I told him I hadn't felt the urge.

"So you only take pictures of war?"

I admitted that that was about the size of it.

"How unhappy you must be."

I told him if it would make him feel better I'd take a series of shots and give them to him, but he answered that his memory was good enough. "We're all ghosts here anyway. We might not even appear in your prints. Just the trees and the sky and no people whatsoever. Only the photographer, you, with his finger on a button."

Two days later Rawlings was back. He'd become lost, he said, while looking for a village where there was said to be some grass. Ending up about twenty kilometers north of the mission, he'd noticed a half-dozen choppers landing at the top of the mountain and had gone closer to see what was what.

"It's a radio station," he told us. "Tower, transmitter, the whole works. Radio Nowhere, man. Must be some pretty heavy wattage up there."

*

I went to Gilliam's cell to justify my existence.

She was out of uniform, in wet hair and a black robe tied with a sash. "I'm not impressed with your empty holster," she said.

"It's a symbol."

"It's pathetic."

Letting out my breath, I went straight to my speech. *One*. It was a game at first, the watching. As in voyeurism. But first I had to see. *Two* was to know what I was seeing. It wasn't always that simple. Sometimes it took years to recognize a photograph. Like some very subtle black joke, it could turn in my mind forever and then I'd unloose a spring or two and just plain get it. *Three*. To get rid of it, to give away the image so that it's no longer in your possession. "But I was wrong. Publication is just a reproduction of those images, a multiplication. I thought it would be a subtraction, me minus the vision. I haven't yet come to *four*."

Gilliam said, "I like your arithmetic but it's all a bit too fancy. You're pretty handy at self-invention, aren't you?"

More words for me to misunderstand. I mumbled something about not wanting her to go on loathing me. "I'd feel better if we were friends."

She only laughed. "Why? Because I'm not a gook?"

"I didn't say that."

"Because I'm white and a nurse and just sitting here alone in my lonesome little cell?"

I was thinking, Whatever home is it's beyond these walls. Still on my feet, I edged backward, trying desperately to become one of Dorn's ghosts. But Gilliam wasn't through with me.

"The mission is finished, Page. Fifteen years he's been here, old man Dorn, but with that radio station up there the Cong isn't going to tolerate him much longer. No more farm and no more sanctuary for the orphans. We may have weeks or we may only have days. There are people to house and to feed, Page. Can you dig that? That might be your *four* if you weren't so damned blind. You could have come to say you'd help, that you wanted to know what you could do, instead of coming in here with this lame business about *one, two,* and *three* and trying to make me fuck with you."

I was already at the door but she rose to hold me there. Her eyes were fierce with a rage I could not measure. The roundest eyes in Asia. "What could be worse, Page, than being a voyeur? Killing these people with bullets instead of with *film*? And you feel no shame? Shame, Page. Shame that no amount of *one* and *two* and *three* can wash clean. Put that in your empty holster."

No use showing her the clippings about my art. I had evidence of a soul but no way of convincing anyone that it was genuine. Dorn had tasted my sweat a final time and said, "*Dao*, still," and it should have been confirmation enough. But that woman got shrill and reminded me that I was first of all an animal. First, second, third, and fourth.

When Dorn disappeared I was one of the search party, humping up and down the mountain paths calling his name. After three days of finding nothing, we got the message. We holed up in the mission and waited for the mail, and when it arrived it was even heavier than we'd expected. Eyes, ears, nose, and tongue of the man came in an American body bag; this gesture of murder wearing an especially gruesome grin. So much for Dorn and my newfound *dao*. When I tasted my own sweat that night it was bitter and cold.

The mortar attack came at dawn, about the time I was gathering the orphans for Gestures. We hurried out of the mission and into the glen and watched those carbon explosions tear apart the cell walls where monks had first prayed three centuries before, set fire to the granary, and pock the courtyard with shallow craters. The shelling lasted for nearly an hour, and when it was finished I didn't know what else to do, so I led the children in Gestures, closing my eyes as Dorn had done but finding myself unable to keep them closed. The children were moving about the glen with arms upraised, swan, trailing downward, flower bud, lifting upward into bloom, tiger, dragon, tree, bird. When I was certain there would be no more shelling, I led them up the path to the mission and gave them over to Recon for safekeeping.

The courtyard was littered with the dead and I looked them all over, thinking of Gilliam. She wasn't there but Rawlings was, in a sprawl near the center of the yard. He'd taken shrapnel above the eye, in the neck, in the shoulder, and in the ribs. Blood was everywhere but he was still alive. Somebody shot him with morphine and we lifted him to a stretcher. He wouldn't shut up, saying it hadn't been his idea to come, it was his father's. "It was *his* idea. *He* said to come. Not me. Him. It was him." I had already walked away but he called me back and asked me to take a picture. "Like this. Take one of me just like this and send it to the bastard. In color, Page. *Do it!*"

My Nikon was crushed under rubble but the Leica was miraculously intact. After setting the distance and the focus, I took five shots without looking through the lens. Seen at an angle, the scene was a mass of red. Gilliam watched me doing it and I swore there was repentance in her eyes.

The photograph was published in an English magazine for which I didn't have credentials. The caption read: *It Wasn't My Idea.*

3

NEW YORK

1967

Back in New York, one could pretty well assume that living through a day was a sure thing. It was the first time I ever felt disappointment in my surroundings.

I was easily bored, and if every picture tells a story I must have been a depraved windbag, selling off the contents of my Vietnam portfolio to a smug but bloodthirsty public. Gilliam was right. I couldn't rid myself of shame. My hands were filthy with the money, and to eliminate some of it I hired a private detective to look for my father. A hopeless enterprise. I knew it even then but there was, still, that immaculate dream of finding him and touching him, and even more than that the wish to be certain that he was not just some anonymous dud, one of Lela's awful and regretted nocturnal mistakes, but a man she'd loved. I hoped never to have to settle on a version of the monikers *bastard, mutt, love child*. The words varied according to the company I kept and the only label I would ever accept was *son*. *Son of*. Armand's family name was fine, but a stricter sense of self-identification was desired. All the same, after paying the detective for six futile months, I added up his charter flights and his cocktails and inevitably subtracted him from the payroll. I was going to have to find that name on my own.

During my sojourn in New York I was a hotel dweller and the ironies of fact (foreign in my own country, rich and unemployed, at war in a land of peace) were all getting lost in the cracks of my disintegrating career path. A stint at Columbia filled time without filling the gaps in my character and for a kick I got myself maced and busted at an antiwar rally, then busted again for possession at a rock concert.

Messages were piling up on the nightstand and for a few months I let them yellow in the sunlight. One fading February evening, short on grass and long on boredom with NBC, CBS, and ABC, I sorted out my masses of paper, and the next day settled a contract for a spread on a Paris dog show. All expenses paid, said the telex. Not my scene, but I was decidedly short on sincerity at the time. Any affluent port in a philosophical storm, I reasoned. You are what you're paid for.

4
PARIS
1967

After only a week my coming and going was beginning to take its toll on my sense of humor. Sitting on the terrace near Saint-Germain, I listened to a bum's description of his life as minister of pigeons, fascinating stuff about toe counts and bread intake, and all I could say was, No shit? He was carrying a stick the size of a Louisville slugger and announced that his new job was mutt hunter. Did I want to join him? No? Then would I contribute to the cause?

When I told him I had an angle on a grenade launcher, model M-79, Marine issue, he shuffled up the road. One crazy outdoing another with a vengeance. He even went so far as to point me out to a *gendarme*, and I sensed that the masses in whom I could confide were beginning to dwindle.

The dog show was over and my prints had been shipped to New York along with text by an English cognoscente. An Italian-bred Irish setter had taken the cake for the third year running. I'd even used a tripod for a set-up session, thinking all the while of Rawlings's advice. The focus had been impeccable and upon receipt of the contact sheets the magazine had wired the balance of my ridiculous fee. With the money as a cushion, I slipped back into my comfortable rut and let the waiting overtake me.

A married French journalist visited my hotel from time to time for athletic bouts of infidelity more closely resembling those bogus televised wrestling matches than sincere unbridled passion. When I came up wanting in the oral department, my lack of spit and tenderness showing me to be just another savage Yank, she gave me the gate. Freedom restored, I took a long bike trip to and from the Rhone Valley, amazing my jaded self with a newly acquired sense of distance, all places now being measured by their proximity to the green world of Nam I'd left behind. Riding like the wind, I felt less ugly and more cleansed, less a fraction of myself than before. In the darkness there were no shadows to run me down and the stars were no longer cluster bombs but sudden still cold points of geometry that I was looking at as if for the first time. I suffered a sweet loneliness for three long weeks, and only when the cash I'd brought along began to run thin did I head back for Paris.

It was June 8, 1967. History freaks may already have made the connection. I slept like a stone and awakened in my hotel room at noon on the 9th, ordered coffee and a newspaper, and read for the first time about the war raging in the Sinai.

Immediately I placed a call to Time/Life for the OK and booked a flight for the following day, destination Jerusalem. *Licking the stamp with a flourish, the snowball addresses itself to hell.*

And on the seventh day they named it the Six Day War. There was no advance billing and I couldn't ask for my money back. All the same, I hung around Jerusalem for the festivities, getting some prints of Moshe Dayan and Golda Meir, twin towers of clenched teeth but with the inevitable pleasure and satisfaction of their victory showing through. Us against all of them, inc. None of my photographs were published but the Hilton was paid in full, and at the very least I had chosen the victorious capital. Anyway, the mere thought that I'd ridden a bicycle alone through the duration of a multinational war was almost too much to believe. When I heard that much of the fighting had been televised I began to realize that my century was evolving too quickly, too abruptly, and that from there on any photos I might produce could turn to sepia overnight. If on the seventh day they named it the Six Day War, the process was getting uncomfortably perfecto. Next thing I knew they'd be booking Yankee Stadium for the Big One with that long-awaited Roman numeral III, and I'd be lucky to get credentials for the parking lot.

Drunken rambling led to exhausting pilgrimlike walks to and from the Wailing Wall, and after a week of this I had to admit to myself that I was getting itchy for something other than despair in the Holy Land. Sainthood was beyond me, so I booked a flight for home and slept fitfully through the long journey, the plane heading against the arc of the sun so that night was hyphenated into a three-hour joke, one day becoming another before the stewardess could screw out the orange juice. Near noon I arrived, hungover and happy, in the ancient and besieged city of Saigon. In plenty of time for Khe Sanh.

IN WHICH PAGE BECOMES AN OLD MAN

The pain and terror are receding like a cheap drug and whatever was wrong with me is less wrong today. Whatever Jane has done (we'll call it healing) has begun to take hold and the word *love* no longer sticks like a bone in my throat if I feel inclined to say it. At least I haven't gone screaming out of her apartment in the dead of night, nor have I needed a quart of Jack Daniel's to lay me down to blessed sleep. Jane exhibits tender Zen; she doesn't take matters to the extreme. I mean, she isn't washing my feet with her hair or any of that, but she isn't nagging me to wash the dishes either. The only thing that riles her is my insistence that I sleep on the floor. We tried making it in her bed just once and I swear I grew seasick. "It's all in your head, Hunter."

"Since when do you call me by my first name?"

"Since we set a wedding date."

I said I was now and forever Page. "Hunter is the baby's name. Him."

What we call ourselves makes a tragic difference to our points of view. Yesterday I was an orphan and today I'm Dada. I inventory myself for a remembered bleeding, imagining shrapnel where there isn't any. It's over now, the worst of it, but not the dreaming. In one of my dreams I open a fleshy zipper and parts of me fall to the floor, organs I can't recognize since I know nothing of anatomy. So I put everything back in a scrambled order and thereafter hear with my knees and speak with my navel. It isn't all that clear as dreams go, but it's faithful; forever near. Each night, falling to sleep, I expect to wake up screaming bloody murder but it never happens. Jane says only that I snarl like a mutt over meat. This would be troubling news if I could hear myself, but there are other sounds to fret over. I freeze when the phone rings, wondering if it's that ghost or the law. Since I'm hiding from both, Jane does all the answering.

"It was him again."

"Which him?"

"Your father."

"Can't be. You said he has an accent."

"He can't help that. He's Spanish."

"And I'm Irish Catholic. He was misinformed."

Jane persists. She has this weakness for strays and cripples, anything of humanity that's been reduced to small print. "I think he's calling from a hospital."

She always knows the cutting words and I have the feeling that something in this news smacks of calculation. Hospitals meaning mortality, a notion I go for in a big way. "Next," I answer, "you'll tell me he's dying."

"How should I know? Why don't you go find out?"

Of course, I don't. I have business with Weatherstone and that aura of his. Two nights of rain have hindered operations but tonight the sky is clear and light. The full moon seems to have erased half the stars, and those that are left are limp and sputtering. The galaxy is getting old, I'm thinking, as I prepare my cameras. By the time we're ready to travel her length and width, only wrinkles will be left to greet us, and vast sighing distances. We will discover we are the only ones here and the loneliness will kill us.

Weatherstone has come and gone, picking up a new set of prints and leaving instructions for a next series. "Vary the focus from time to time, just to see what gives."

I asked him, "What focus? I don't have a point of reference to aim for. Just that blank sky."

Weatherstone said to look more closely. To see past seeing. To squint, to blink. "On the unholy oblique, Mr. Page. The heavens have their own uncharted countryside: contour, hill and dale. You may see nothing but shadows in your photos but *I* can recognize what's there. Keep up the good work. I've never seen such purple before as in those bruised clouds over the Bronx. I have to tell you, I'm very encouraged."

I reached to my temple and dialed a number, but the gesture was lost on Weatherstone. Before climbing back into his Lear jet, he wrote another check and I turned it over to Jane. "Live it up, sweetheart. The end is at hand."

Smoking Colombian, I gaze across the rooftops and listen to the snap and whir of the timed cameras, feeling literally on top of things, all along the watchtower. The surprise of sitting so high up in the most populous city in America is that you don't see any people, just the high rises in which they live and work, buy and sell, fuck, snore, eat, and die. Humanity is reduced to geometric units, cubes and cylinders, and you can almost forget the sweat and blood and bone that dwell within. If there is smoke in the distance, some housing project burning, it is that distance that keeps you from spilling your guts in sorrow. You might hear the ambulance wailing but you can't see the body bag with the foot sticking out.

I watch the lights and the moving cars and convince myself that I am the only one of God's children still living in the city of stone. If they want me, my accusers, they'll have to climb up here to get me. I can take their pictures to show them their empty eyes. And I'll still have the option of jumping before they take me. Which option is ever there, like a hair trigger. I keep my distance from the edge of the roof.

Gabriel says they won't buy my pictures, the new set. The consensus, he tells me, is that I've gone soft somewhere essential. That my art has gotten sentimental. I tell him it's only a matter of expectations. You see my name in the credits and you're expecting bloodshed and mayhem.

"So what would happen if the serial killer, in prison for life, began writing poetry that rivaled Emily Dickinson's? They'd wrap fish and chips with his pages; you can put money on it."

Gabriel makes no effort to soothe my frayed nerves. "No one wants you turning over a new leaf, Page. You're in show business and the rules say you give the public what it wants."

"Which is?"

"Evidence of the victims. Food for sleep. Proof that the dying is going on on the *other* side of the sea. Though some people think your work is just sleight-of-hand, fancy cutting and overlays. It's hard to believe what you're saying you've seen."

I am trying to hold my head in my hands, a gesture preliminary to weeping.

"The trouble is, Page, these new pictures are more like candidates for Hallmark cards. To a swell dad. Thinking of you. Or better, thou."

"Thee."

"You get my point."

I do but I disagree. "Those are down-home snapshots, Gabriel. Did you like the one of the Montagnards having a cookout?"

"Very homey, Page."

"That was monkey they were roasting. I ate the eyeballs myself, out of the superstition that I might see something new."

"I'm sold, Page. Really. But the editors won't bite."

I've explained how I got my start in the business. So you'll understand that this rejected collection was a belated apology. I simply took the pictures I'd missed the first time around, the ones with living people in them.

Gabriel says I've really gone out of my way to offend people. My story isn't ending the way they'd planned. For one thing, I'm not dead.

I admit to him that I lied. "About the eyes. I didn't eat them."

"Maybe you should have."

"I lost my nerve."

He buys me another drink. "So what do you do next?"

"I beat you to within an inch of your life for not having the guts to print my stuff. Then I wipe my brow with your silk handkerchief and stride out of this bar and into a future of silver linings."

"I'm not your target, Page, I'm just a spectator."

"The innocent bystander?"

"If you'd died I'd have come to the funeral."

I don't have a comeback to this. He is, I realize, sincere. Looking at me as already deceased in some odd way, he's lost without that ceremony and doesn't know quite how to do me honor.

The truth of it is, we're all going to live forever. That sound we're hearing overhead is not a chopper but the furious wingbeat of the American archangel. My father is in heaven and hallowed be his name. Trespassing on government property, I wander to a children's playground and sit for a while on a bench to watch the kiddies at play. Their faces please me no end, all that surprise and delight over sand piles, monkey bars, and a rusty teeter-totter. I have lit a cigarette and leaned back, ready for sleep and a sweet dream or two, when I notice that the sky is empty of stars, no surprise in daytime, and not a single cloud is there to relieve me of the blue. I sit forward to watch the children again and already the scene has changed. One kid takes a truck to the head of another, drawing blood, and there follows a rapid catfight between two Puerto Rican women. Putting out my cigarette, I realize that if the war lasts long enough some of these kids will soon be torching gooks or spraying hooches with M-16 fire. Hunter, too, if I can't get the word to him.

I was going to say. I was saying. The truth of it is that we are all going to live forever from sea to shining sea. If I am not yet dead I must be giving a marvelous performance. All I really mean to be is less careless and more grateful that I haven't ended up a miserable shell-shocked basket case, one of those guys in pee-stained underwear unable to get out of bed without crying like a baby. I already had Hunter and now I've got Jane. Somewhere in the equation is a gift about which I harbor suspicion. It's as though ever since I could see I've been waiting to go blind, but for the moment the tragedy has failed to unfold. I have sleep-walked through the valley of easy death and am still upright, living forever.

At night I dream again and again of the parts of me unraveling. Two out of three times I am unable to put myself back together. The third time I succeed in fashioning a new self. One who will love me.

To my paternal shame, I spoon too-hot oatmeal into Hunter's pink mouth and his wailing lays a curse on me that will outlive the day. Jane is gone to work and the sitter, Teresa, is doing the shopping. I am alone with Hunter and he takes a long time to forgive me. When the phone starts ringing, I forget myself and answer it.

"Is this Hunter Page?"

Lying would be an act of wisdom but I am slow on my feet. "Speaking."

"We have a proposal to make."

"We?"

"The United States Marine Corps."

"I'm listening."

"We would like you to present yourself, at your leisure, within the next forty-eight hours, to Mr. Randall of Intelligence. Do you have a pen?"

I copy down a midtown address and phone number. "I suppose there is a choice involved. An either/or of some kind."

"We'd simply like to ask you a few questions."

I reply that I don't give interviews. "No comment to whatever you want to know."

The voice wants to know when I might be expected and I answer that I might be out of town. "I've got this honeymoon to attend. You know how it is."

Finishing with some phrases about not taking rain checks, the voice hangs up.

I awaken on Jane's floor and am alone. The room has that aquarium glow of unnatural light, neither sun nor moon, Manhattan's pink and blue neon coming through the walls. I rise and go into the kitchen to read the clock over the stove. Three in the morning, for whatever it's worth. Jane's kitchen. Fake-wood cabinets and Formica counters; peppermill and potholders, cookbook and spice rack. I am sweating despite the September breeze and choke back a terror induced by the sight of my own self in a photograph pinned next to the cutting board. Not my own work but Jane's, a Polaroid from a previous visit: Page in trenchcoat standing in a field. The original cigar-store Indian left in the snow. So this is what she sees when she washes the dishes. I have no memory of snow or of the cold. Filling a whisky glass, I get started on another litany of my life, tracing the here and there to what brings me to a kitchen in a high rise at three in the morning. The same old story keeps getting told, and by the time the whisky glass is empty the only thing I regret is that it isn't still full.

Going to Hunter's room, I keep a close eye on him for a long while and consider how things will be better for us now, for myself and my tribe. I will be normal, will sleep dreamlessly and awaken to coffee and the sports page, and my wife will wear pins in her hair that I will remove one by one, undoing her. I carry this vision with me into Jane's room and search the sudden darkness for her body. She sleeps in beds and I am the savage. Turning back the sheet, I join her there and my arrival awakens her. She burrows into me and kisses my shoulder. The trance begins and we move together, making somnambulant love that ends with her small cry. Afterward, I imagine that her eyes are wet, but when I touch her lids they are dry. Her face to my chest, she says I'm healed, and though it may be simply an imitation of good health, a momentary loss of tragic gravity, I am inclined to believe her. And so sleep in the circle of her arms, in her bed, in her city, in America, etc.

I seem to be reinventing myself and feel as if I'm doing more than going through the motions. At the very least I'm not kidding when I hold Hunter tight against my chest and feel a sunburst in the vicinity of the heart.

Stepping out onto the sidewalk, I see a man in a wheelchair across the street, a white-shirted attendant behind him. They are looking in my direction and I have this premonition, so I head down the street in a kind of limping trot, cruising speed for the gimp I've become. But somehow the attendant catches up with me, having left the man in the wheelchair behind. He reaches for my arm as if he wants something and I tell him I'm all out of quarters.

The attendant is about forty-five, seedy despite the white shirt and pants; dirty hair and bad teeth. "I have news for Hunter Page," he says.

"Too bad. I hear he's missing in action."

"You're not him?"

I realize I've got him turned around now. "I was," I tell him.

"Mr. Grace wants to talk to you."

The man has wheeled himself down the block and is waiting across the street. I make a studied attempt not to look his way.

"We've made a long trip," says the attendant. "The old guy is getting wheezy and somebody owes me cabfare."

"What if I just keep running?"

"Listen, pal. I'm just a poor slob on minimum wage. Don't make this hard on me."

"Maybe if I knew what you wanted."

"It's what *he* wants. A powwow of some kind."

"Got a pen and paper?"

"Yeah." He produces them from his pockets.

I write, "No one believes you, least of all me."

The attendant reads the note and says, "I suppose this is fraught with meaning."

"Just deliver it."

"Why do I have the feeling we'll be back?"

"Just don't forget to bring the loaded gun next time."

Two days later, Jane and I are married at City Hall. She wears a yellow summer dress and a flower over her right ear. None of her family received an invitation. Gabriel shakes free for a long lunch so he can play best man, and since I'd had the presence of mind to buy a ring he is not standing there empty-handed.

The ceremony has all the sincerity of a cheap greeting card but when I slip that ring onto Jane's finger we are both a trifle giddy. On the front steps, Gabriel throws a handful of rice and Jane hands her clutch of flowers to Teresa, no one else in the vicinity waiting to catch them. In the taxi, about the time I'm realizing that I'm somebody's old man now, Jane announces she'd rather we skip the honeymoon. We've planned a weekend in Atlantic City. "Really, Page. I don't want to leave Hunter."

Nor do I. The idea of splitting up the family, even for a weekend, is unpleasant. Besides, we have documents to sign. The adoption papers are now lying in a drawer waiting for signatures from this *married* couple. Here in the sight of God and the state of New York.

I never said Dune Buggy was white. You just assumed so because I never said he was black. Nor did I ever say he was the father. You assumed so because he was married to Chulin. There is this crucial remnant of fact that I haven't yet revealed to Jane, and I'm working it over in my mind without getting it out from between my teeth. Dune Buggy, by the way, was white, but that doesn't mean he was the father. I've been laying bets with myself for months now without knowing whether I'm even on the track. All that time I lived with the two of them, Dune Buggy and Chulin, I was loving Jane and Chulin both. Geography won out. And when Hunter was born, neither I nor Dune Buggy could find a signature on his person, any form of birthmark denoting which of us had been there. Since Dune Buggy had married his mother, we had him christened with my name, thus giving him at least a handmade genealogy: a myth rather than an outright lie.

When the papers are signed and stamped, we begin a six-week waiting period at the end of which, if the inquiry comes up with nothing criminal in either of our pasts, Jane and I will be lawful parents. There is a pointy irony to adopting what may be my own son but I'm not in a mood to nail myself to the cross of truth just to avoid it.

*

A few days after the wedding, I'm limping uptown when, at the corner of Broadway and 88th, I stumble upon that man in his wheelchair. His lunatic attendant is waiting nearby but I don't see any sign of a gun. The old man says he wants to talk to me. His accent is Spanish so I know he's the ghost. When I tell him I've got to be going he says there isn't time.

"My name is Baptiste," he says.

I tell him I heard he was Grace.

"Now I am. But I once was Baptiste."

"What does this have to do with me?"

"I knew your mother in England. They told me I'm your father."

He has white hair and dark piercing eyes. I'd expected senility but he isn't exhibiting any. He is holding a manila envelope on his lap and I'm hoping he won't open it.

"I've heard all this before," I tell him.

"I know. I have evidence."

Suddenly I'm hot. "Why are you doing this?" I shout at him. "Who's paying you?" Then I realize a crowd is gathering and I begin to edge away.

The attendant grabs my arm to hold me there. "I don't want to hurt you," he tells me.

"Think of something else then." Turning to the old man, I say, "I advise you to get back in your bed. You need rest and you've got the wrong man here."

That immaculate dream of touching him, of hearing his voice.

He says he is an artist. Or was. "Until I lost the heart of it. I've been looking for you for a long time. I am holding your passport. I can show you."

This makes no sense to me, and my feet are moving before I know it. When the attendant reaches for my arm again I give him the back of my hand. No one follows me as I walk away but it doesn't matter. Wherever I'm headed I'm taking myself along. With each limping step I feel like turning back and holding out my arms to him like oars into deep water; all right, I'm listening. But by the time I circle the block he is already at the far end of the street and the attendant is lifting him, chair and all, into the back of a station wagon. There is time enough to catch up but those seconds pass like gunshots until the chamber is empty and the station wagon has vanished in the noontime traffic.

Rumor has it that I called out to him. That I went to his side and knelt down before his wheelchair, laying my head on his knees. A rumor like that candle you light instead of cursing the legendary darkness. Closing my eyes, I feel his hand on my forehead. "Where are we?" I ask him.

"Nineteen forty-four."

"Is that a year or an address?"

"One or the other," he answers. As though it makes any difference.

BAPTISTE IN LOVE

ENGLAND

1944

Lieutenant Baptiste, answering these days to the pseudonym Miguel Otero, turns left off the rain-slick motorway and onto a dirt-and-gravel stretch of road, aiming his jeep toward the Mother of Mercy Clinic. Sitting erect, the steel brace around his back making it difficult for him to turn his head, he grips the wheel tightly with his fists as the jeep bounces over a series of potholes, the shocks sending red sparks of pain up and down his spine. Already he is a half-hour late for his treatment, having waited in vain for the English fog to lift, and now the road before him is disintegrating beneath a rain that has been falling for what seems an eternity.

The wound is an old one, a souvenir from the fall of Barcelona, a burden that he carries too literally on his back, but recent surgery has left a new and fascinating scar, a dotted scarlet stripe from the cleft of his buttocks to the base of his neck like a line of demarcation. He has been aerated and relieved of one hundred and thirty tiny bits of Franco's shrapnel, lodged like confetti from belt-line to nape of neck, resembling, beneath the overgrowth of new skin, lavender freckles, birthmarks, or love bites. The doctors have massaged and straightened his vertebrae, sliced away scar tissue, and then sewn up the wound like the cloth skin of a rag doll, the stuffing rearranged just so. Two months in absolute traction have been followed by three months in the steel brace, and Dr. Runtley tells him that in another month, maybe less, he will be fitted for a simpler and more flexible binding. In the meantime, an old and by-now-tiring joke passes between them from day to day, the doctor saying, "Don't do it unless the woman is on top." To which Baptiste is supposed to raise his eyebrows slightly, smile, and answer, "But what do I do with the other woman?" To which Dr. Runtley laughs, slaps his back, youch, calling him a sly devil, har de har, must be that Mediterranean blood, eh, Miguel?

Baptiste is, in point of fact, Castilian, but hasn't seen his place of birth since 1938, when he crossed the border to Perpignan and began the first of his two exiles. France housed him after Franco's triumph and he stayed until June of 1940, working at photographic assignments, gathering witness accounts of the civil war for communist pamphlets, waiting tables at a brasserie in the Marais, bartending, day-laboring; a living if not a life, but he'd had no complaints. When France fell to the Nazis, he'd hung back, living just north of Paris in the suburb of Saint-Ouen, and waited for the fledgling resistance to locate him, offer him a position in the firm, and send him into subterranean battle. Within six months he'd made contact with Roux, a leader of the communist resistance, and was employed primarily as a runner and code man, passing through Paris on a rusty bicycle to deliver messsages in one code and return replies in another. The meaning of the messages was never revealed to him, leaving him in a doubly perilous position. Had he been captured, he'd have had no information with which to barter for his life. Simply numbers and letters, binaries, octets, each of them as incomprehensible to him as a foreign language or the static of a radio trapped between frequencies. Early in 1942, he'd been sent across the Channel to make contact with an English sympathizer offering money and arms, but the man had been arrested as a spy before Baptiste could get to him. Instead of turning around and heading back to Roux and the Paris underground, he'd shed his communist trappings and joined up with de Gaulle's Free French Forces, where, within a space of months, he became a Channel-runner.

The art of Channel-running is in the depth and range of roles to be played out. Peasant, day laborer, steelworker, miner—any change of face to meet the moment. Baptiste's favorite guise, and long his most effective, is that of village idiot. The mechanics are simple enough: a limp, a lolling tongue, vacant eyes. His idiocy is cover for his accent; he speaks French with animal growls interspersed among the *moi, je*. The only unpleasant part is shitting in his own pants, a necessary ploy to create the stink that allows him, in crowded train stations most particularly, a wide berth. Brussels, Liège, Lille, Rouen, and Paris have been his principal routes, and like a hundred other Channel-runners he's found that the risk is always relative to the length of stay. On some occasions, he's made the round trip in a matter of days, slipping packets of money to resistance contacts, for example, then turning back and heading for a boat off the Dutch coast. It is the multiple-task routines that wear most on his nerves, requiring several changes of roles and disguises, the derelict limping into a latrine and emerging minutes later in a double-breasted suit, his tie held neatly in place with a silver pin, *mouchoir* fluffed upward from his breast pocket, *but the same limp* and his tongue still dangling wetly from his mouth. He'd once crossed himself up this way in Paris, at the Gare du Nord, first noticing his oversight after a full half-hour. Dangerous, that slipup. Perhaps only the night, newly darkened by the occupation, had covered his mistakes. At any rate, his heart had never beat faster, thrumming something flamenco as he'd made his way down the tenth *arrondissement* to a rendezvous at the Opéra.

The crossings are always the worst part, the waiting for long hours in a freezing shack, covered in rags, shivering and cursing the human nation, eyes searching through fogged glass for an approaching trawler—what would be the signal this time? a swaying yellow lantern—and then someone offering him a thermos, usually tea when he'd have preferred black coffee, something to warm his bones while the boat rocked back against the current, the motor geared down low, almost idling so as not to leave a wakę or anything detectable from the air. *Crawling* to the other side while some Irishman up front is muttering, Hail Mary full of grace, the Lord is with thee; they hear an occasional droning overhead and someone says Messerschmitt, but the Irishman says it couldn't be, it's flying too high, maybe a Yank bomber, maybe a reconnaissance plane, maybe an angel. When they reach the coast at dawn they are searched by the British shore patrol, stem to stern and pocket to crotch; one never knows one's friend or enemy, does one?

His back, always fragile since that mortar hit in Barcelona, finally caved in during a run through Brittany. His final contact had hidden him in a creaky loft and the loose boards, rotted with age, had collapsed in the night, throwing him to the cold floor. He'd been driven immediately to the coast and abandoned on the beach, where he'd spent a terrifying afternoon in the sight of God, unable to walk or crawl back toward the nearest treeline. After digging a hole at his side, he'd slid into it and pulled sand over his legs and waist and torso, then waited, imitating a seashell, for the tide to come in and bring rescue.

Arriving at the clinic, he parks the jeep up front, climbs painfully from behind the wheel, and heads in for his daily treatment. An hour in the whirlpool followed by a half-hour of stretching exercises, an indifferent massage from a nurse's aide, more stretching exercises, then a brief examination by Dr. Runtley.

"The X-rays show that you're on the mend. Brace giving you any trouble?"

"The same as before."

"Only while screwing, is that it?" A fat wink at the Spaniard.

"I'm looking forward to taking it off."

"Can't rush it, young man. You want it to mend straight, I'm sure. Wouldn't want your spine to go funny on you. Need a straight line; no diversions, no squiggles."

Runtley calls Baptiste *young man*, although Baptiste is past forty and the doctor is younger by at least five years. "It's your pretty face," Runtley tells him. "That high forehead and big brown eyes. The sun has given you a color no Englishman could ever hope to have. Me, I'm all used up. Never was pretty to begin with and now just take a look. No hair, too much fat, bad teeth. The RAF wouldn't take me, not even to work in one of their clinics. I drink too much and I still can't get to sleep at night. Sometimes I blame it on the war but most of the time I know better."

Baptiste is inclined to forget about the war. In the Midlands, he is as far from it as he has ever been. In London there are air raids, sirens and searchlights, little fires always burning in the distance, the eternal smell of smoke. On the Continent, people have a way of crossing streets at full speed, doors are closed and locked tight, windows shuttered, lights extinguished. Baptiste catalogs a lifetime's store of small regrets, and the most pressing these days is the company's interdiction of his picture-taking while out on a run. The vacant cities, so tragic under occupation, are already faded to a worldly black and white; such a natural drabness, as though all color has been absorbed into time, faded to sepia, vanished. From one street to another are intermittent darknesses, charcoal shadings, the pencilwork of despair. But here in the English Midlands there is still a breath of color, especially now that the winter has rolled back like a dirty sheet and here and there crocuses are sprouting at the foot of brick walls, on the borders of front steps, in flower boxes, gay little blooms meaning nothing to Baptiste except that they are not black and white and the war is not here and now, and then he is inclined to let the whole affair just slip from his mind.

He lives in a tiny village called Rockenham, secluded from the motorway—bypassed, as it were—remaining nestled in a patch of woods where there's been no hunting worth speaking of for more than a century. A number of wounded runners are housed there, as well as some British officers, and Baptiste's room at the bed-and-breakfast is on the ground floor since he can't manage stairways, both an honor and a pleasure, in that his comfort is assured. He has a room to himself, a window looking out on trees, a hard bed, a desk and dresser. He is awakened each morning by the sounds of the housemaid in the kitchen next door, her pots and pans, the banging of cupboards. Reveille. She stirs up a vat of oatmeal, bakes scones, puts the kettle on to boil, then raps on his door: "Mr. Otero, your time has come." The war is elsewhere. Lacing his fingers behind his head, he gazes toward the ceiling, measuring its distance. Twice a week the wounded runners gather for intelligence meetings, during which they are brought up to date on shifts in the network, code-phrase sequences, minor triumphs, or the death or capture of various of their comrades. The rest of the time Baptiste is on his own, free to wander through the village or take a jeep to the clinic or to Northampton, where the pubs stay open later. For his own security, he is told, he must keep up his identity as Miguel Otero, a fallen aviator and not an intelligence runner. The pseudonym is both an exaggeration of form, secrecy becoming a habit rather than a practice, and a way of staying sharp, of keeping in touch with a role, any role, rather than letting the man he is emerge into the light of day. For three months he has been Miguel, while Baptiste remains half buried in sand, still waiting on that beach, looking seaward for a ship. The war is a newspaper, a radio, or rumors in a pub. Once, and only once, has it come to Rockenham. A German bomber strayed too far north, lost, no doubt, and obviously crippled, as evidenced by a trailing plume of black smoke. The pilot had let fall a single bomb before crashing into a stony field north of the village, and the bomb had left a harmless crater, twenty feet by twenty, in the village square. Within days the townspeople had built a white picket fence around the crater, gathered up splinters of bomb and put them into a glass case, and constructed a monument around the site.

"Sometimes," Runtley is saying, "I'm happy they wouldn't have me. What would I have done in the war besides get myself killed? Still, they are always looking at me in an odd way, a man my age and not in uniform. My loyalty to the nation is under scutiny, my morals, my personal habits. They want to see sacrifice, my countrymen. They want to see suffering as proof of my allegiance. I can only show them cardiograms, traces on a graph paper that spell out a murmur of the heart. It's not enough, I'm told. Only figures, documents, medical opinions. I admit, Miguel, I could use a friend, someone in whom I could confide. Can you come to supper tonight? I will call my wife and tell her to set a place."

Baptiste says no, he is already committed.

"A woman, I take it."

Baptiste nods.

"Remember what I told you."

"About the brace."

"She's to be . . ."

"On top."

"Good lad. Off with you, then." They shake hands quickly and Baptiste walks out of the office, hearing, as the door is closing behind him, "You lucky bastard."

Late in the afternoon the fog disperses to reveal a forlorn, flagging sunset down below the treeline. Daylight lasts the time it takes Baptiste to climb back into his jeep, pat pockets for keys, adjust the rear-view, and slip into gear. As he turns onto the dirt road, already bracing for the upcoming potholes, the sun sinks a last notch and all around him there is darkness.

England, not this war, will be the death of me.

He looks forward with all his heart to the final run across the Channel, the last mission, certain as he is that the rain will still be falling on the Midlands long after the peace is signed and the prisoners of war identified, processed, and sent trudging homeward.

By which time I will be as white as any English spook. The very image of Dr. Runtley, him of the murmuring heart.

He drives faster, as though in pursuit of the setting sun, vaulting the jeep from pothole to pothole, but pulls up short at the motorway. Turning left, he heads northward in the direction of Northampton. There are hedgerows to either side of him, overgrown, long untended; there's a war on and all the gardeners are in uniform, off in Bristol somewhere with rakes and shovels, tending to the airstrip, saluting marigolds; there's a war on and all the gardens are gone to hell. Sticky-wet branches thwack the jeep in passing and the trees weep a late mist over the asphalt. The air itself is still moist as a breath, wetting Baptiste's cheeks and forehead, the wind dragging droplets together into tears. But he is not weeping, has not wept since he left Spain. *There* was the rending, the shedding, the keening: monody, threnody, and jeremiad. The down-to-the-knees outpouring, nightlong lamentations over a universe come to a sudden end. There, *there*, but not here. Here there is only this English mist like a lace across his eyes, a fine tinsel at the corner of each eyelid, something in his chest sagging and warping at the merest thought of España or of anything dry, any sun-touched pair of arms, or the strummed sounds of his native tongue.

Coming to another side road, he pulls off the motorway, follows a gravel path down into a dripping glen, and parks the jeep in front of the Blue Lantern pub. He lifts his frame from behind the wheel and sets his feet into mud, stops to adjust his tie and cap, and notes for the first time a speckle of rust on his supposedly stainless-steel brace. Then he wipes the last kiss of rain from his mustache and strides into the pub like an officer, his eyes casting around the two crowded rooms for Ariel.

He wends his way around the bar, moves toward the larger room in the back, and finds her already seated at a corner table; her eyes find his at the same moment. Standing to embrace him, she has to lift herself high on her toes since he can barely bend to meet her, and the kiss is a swift brushing of lips. Baptiste settles into a chair beside her and leans back to look at her, the first welcome sight of the day. She is wearing a hat, a flowered bonnet that doesn't much please him, and he asks her to take it off.

"Oh, this?" She reaches to remove the pins. "I forgot. I put it on to keep out the rain."

Nothing, Baptiste is thinking, can keep out the rain. But a moment later, looking into her eyes, he reconsiders; *si*. He is used to heavier women, women with strong legs and breasts that overflow his hands. Ariel is slight, small-chested, a surprise to his arms. Without the hat, her dark hair falls to just below the shoulder, and she brushes it back, pulling the length of it tight over her forehead and securing it behind her ears with a barrette. Like a *señorita.* Close enough now, he leans to give her a longer kiss, a strange custom to the English, this kissing in public. She is not displeased.

"Have you been waiting long?"

"Only a few minutes. Shall we order dinner here or go elsewhere?"

"I'll leave you to decide."

"Here, then. I'm in a hurry."

"What for?"

She tells him she has secured a place for the night, a cottage only a few miles away. "It belongs to a friend of a friend but he's away, in the army. Can you stay the night? No bed checks at the bed-and-breakfast?"

He says he is a free man.

"Not until morning."

They order beer while waiting for dinner and before the first pint is drained each has a hand on the other's leg, something vital in the connection, the earth spinning so quickly that each feels, in the presence of the other, the need to hang on to something. It has been this way from the beginning, a beer or two at the pub, a fast dinner someplace, and then off to the nearest country inn for a night of lovemaking, smoke rising from the bedsheet, sparks and embers, Ariel lighting a Player's in the darkness and smoking it by herself and by the time the cigarette has burned to its end she is already reaching for him, moving over him, holding him in both hands and descending, descending. There's a war on and bombs fall in the distance, too far away to be heard, but the tremor is felt all the same. Ariel asking if, when he gets his wrapping, *he* will be on top? "Not that I mind. I like it this way. You?"

Sí, yo también.

He met her at the clinic, where she was getting treatment, but for what malady she has never agreed to tell him. "A disease," is all she says. "But not even really that."

"Is there pain?"

"Often, yes, but less than there used to be."

"When you're with me?"

"Never."

"Never?"

"Just sometimes," she admits.

He wants to know how.

"When you leave the bed. When you put on your brace. When you button up your uniform and leave me alone and naked in the bed."

"When the war is over . . ."

Her fingers to her lips. "The war is never over."

"I'll know where to find you."

She tells him that he shouldn't. She won't be there. "This is all the love there is in me. This pub, this village, this hotel. The war is just a fancy excuse for us and later we'll both go home and tell lies and never forget."

She likes her mysteries, her elusiveness. She is English, she says, but not from the region. Where, then? South. Near London? Farther south, the far coast.

That explains her accent, Baptiste figures, which is not at all like the accents he hears daily in Rockenham. Once, a man in a pub had referred to her as a Canadian and she'd blushed scarlet, correcting him with a small voice: "I'm English." Her voice had seemed to blossom into a different tone, a cadence of syllables spoken not through her lips but through her teeth. "Not what you say I am."

As with a country, love imposes exiles that only return will undo. Baptiste senses himself forever on the far shore from Ariel except in their common bed, where their thrashing beats back the menace of their parting. Bones will heal and the illness recede. In the meantime, they close the shutters against proof of the rising sun. He is past forty and has loved before and she, too, has the feel of a woman touched by men, numberless and certainly as itching with want of her as he. He begs the night to last all night, loves her, sleeps, and then awakens with flames of pain moving up and down his spine. Slithering from her bed, he reassembles himself on his knees at the foot, finding himself at the level of her parted legs. Leaning forward, he places his lips upon her labia, half kissing and half speaking, love's untranslatable argument to *stay*, stay as long as I need you. Awakened, she locks his head between her legs and he hears nothing more, not even the sounds of his own lapping, nor her cries, nor his own cries lost somewhere in her channel. She will carry the echo of those cries long after his exile has run its course, his broken heart mended, his spine restored.

Along comes the kidney pie and he orders another round of beers, telling her it should be the last, no need to get drunk, they'll buy a bottle of something at the bar on the way out. Ariel, for once, devours the kidney pie, even going so far as to help herself to some of his.

"It's the treatment," she tells him. "I'm getting back my appetite. My taste for things."

Baptiste wonders aloud, testing the waters, just what her treatment might be. Kinetic? Hypnotic? Mystic?

"Chemicals," she answers, the closest she's come to saying anything direct about her visits to the clinic. As though the ice were now broken, she goes on, telling him that she's nearly finished with it all, close to a cure. "They tell me I can leave in another week. Two at the most."

He refuses to ask her where she'll go. He is intimidated by the pub, the strangers all around him. In the cottage, he decides. Once alone, naked, warming each other under the cool sheets, he will ask her.

They finish their beers, pay the bill, and leave. In the jeep, they kiss and feel through each other's clothes. Above them the sky is like a black silk curtain shot with bullet holes, the last of the rain is gone, and there is only a breath of wind to stir the trees. She directs him out of the glen, across the motorway, and down another country road, past the turn for Rockenham, up the north bank of a low hillside, and into a patch of wood where a cottage is nestled. The main room is enormous, with a great wooden beam holding up the ceiling and a wide fireplace yawning across half a wall. A new stack of wood has been set beside it but Baptiste finds it still wet and anyway Ariel is saying no, they don't need a fire, darling, come to bed, we'll light a fire there. She says things like that, perpetual double meanings for their lovemaking: anything having to do with fire, lightning, sparks, heat, combustion. By the time he has closed and bolted the door and crossed to the bedroom she is already naked and waiting for him under the covers. He takes a long time to remove his shoes and pants, unbutton his uniform, and unbuckle the brace, then finally he slides into the bed, landing in her arms. They ignite on contact, hands chasing across each other's bodies until at last she is up and hovering over him, taking him into her with a gasp at the very moment they hear the drone of an airplane overhead, *one of ours*, heading south in search of the rain.

"Miguel?"

"Ariel?"

"When you're better, I mean when your back is healed, what will you do?"

"Go back to the war, I suppose."

"I've never imagined you a part of it, despite your uniform. What do you do in the war? You've never said."

"I'm a runner," he tells her. "I run."

She says she doesn't understand.

"All right, then. I'm a spy."

She laughs into his clavicle. "I can't believe it."

"Why not?"

"Spies are faceless, shadowy. Not the kind of men I'd want to make love to me."

He tells her he is living out a part, disguised in love. "The truth is, my name is not Miguel, and Otero means *other*."

"But they said you were a pilot."

"Who?"

"The doctor at the clinic. Someone else, I forget who."

"Which doctor?"

"Harrow."

Baptiste doesn't know the man. "Is he the one who's treating you?"

She senses the trap too late and answers too slowly. "No."

The rain is falling again, slanting against the unshuttered window—cold, no doubt—this relentless English sorrowful falling.

"Miguel?"

"I'm listening."

"I'm a spy, too. My name isn't Ariel and I . . ."

"No more," he cuts her short.

"I thought you'd want to know."

"I do and I don't. If I know who you are, you'll have to know who I am. Can you live with a secret? It doesn't matter. When this war is over, I'll find you and we'll tell our confessions."

She reminds him that's all she meant to say.

They sleep and awaken twice in the night to make love, her weight hurting his back more than he lets on. In the morning he will get a shot of morphine from Runtley, a lecture, a dig in the ribs—"Incorrigible, eh?"—and will regret nothing. At dawn they drift into a final sleep, but near midmorning he awakens to the sounds of her moving about the room. Though she is already dressed and the day is surprisingly warm, she is shivering and seems unsteady, troubled. He asks her what's the matter.

She doesn't know. "The dawn. The sunlight seems to unravel me."

But there is no sunlight, only a pale glow of daybreak in the room, the color of silver coming through the thin tissue of curtain and calling itself light.

He asks her if she wants to leave. "Are you in a hurry? Someone's expecting you?"

"No one," she says.

Then she should undress and get back into bed. "This is not a hotel. We can stay past noon if we like."

In his arms she is as fragile as he has ever known her, both tender and distant, wishing him closer, but when he leans over her, breathing downward, she resists his lovemaking, wanting to be held, she says, just held.

Sometime past noon, having dozed and awakened, they slip from the bed and dress in separate corners. Then she crosses the foot of the bed to circle him in her arms, hugging him tight. "There you are," she says, "braced, uniformed, a tall row of buttons."

He has an appointment in a half-hour but she wants them to take their time. "Is there anything to drink here?"

He doesn't know. "Look in the kitchen. That's where you English keep it, don't you?"

"Keep what?"

"The whisky."

She says she wouldn't know.

But in a cupboard over the stone sink is a quarter-bottle of Scotch. She pours two glasses, offers one to Baptiste, and they drink to each other, swallowing fire. Then she notices the clock on the wall.

"So late? Already?"

Checking his watch, he confirms. "Half past noon."

"I have a treatment in fifteen minutes."

"To your healing," he says, tipping his glass.

She answers, "Down the hatch."

Minutes later they are in the jeep, ready to resume their separate lives. Revving the engine, Baptiste says something about tonight, same place, and Ariel only nods. Same sun, same indifferent light. He drives her into a horizon he's long since memorized, a sloping hill and a valley beyond, trees to either side, a circular route, hill and dale, and minutes before arriving at the clinic she reaches across the distance and touches his forearm with cool fingers, squeezes briefly, then lets go. Already she is beginning to tell him *adiòs*.

Sun and moon, moon and sun. Baptiste counts the time on his hands and finds it as heavy as those English coins, ponderous, worn smooth. Days of pacing in his room, pointless debriefings at the center, whirlpools, stretching exercises, and finally the release into night, the pub, the cottage, Ariel's thin arms. His recompense for another slow day of survival. Sanctuary from another Channel-crossing. His life gone wooden and surrounded by flames.

The cottage is theirs for a fortnight, a place for them to massage each other's wounds and then bump and nestle among shores of want, turning to lust, turning to tenderness. Ariel runs her thin fingers over his ribs, downward to his hips, thighs, knees, going through an inventory of the whole of him, as though her eyes will not be sufficient to record it all for a later time, as though memory is tactile, of the skin, and not photographic.

They have a way of not speaking to each other. The subjects are objects. Who she is and where she comes from he will never know. And in return, he will remain Miguel to her, the Other, a Spanish officer from an unknown unit. A pawn in white, advancing on a black queen.

One morning she tells him, "This is my last day. My treatments are finished."

"When are you leaving?"

"Very soon."

"Home?"

"Translate, please."

"Home. *La casa*. Where you come from."

She smiles, holding a pose for him. "I suppose," she says, "*home* is a word for where I'm going."

They make love as if in slow motion, each afraid of hurting the other, of digging too deeply, of unearthing old sorrows. Then she dresses quickly, skirt and blouse and flat shoes, and leans to help him with his brace, curling the last loop around its hook until he is tall and rigid, reassembled before her eyes.

"I'll remember everything," she tells him. "I'll be wearing your fingerprints for a very, very long time."

Arriving at the Mother of Mercy Clinic, they go separate ways, he to Runtley's waiting room and she to a different wing. When his treatment is finished, he has the whirlpool, massage, and exercises, and later a shot of morphine from the good doctor. "I've diluted it with something else; a dose of restraint, let's say." Against his every wish Baptiste feels himself falling asleep, his limbs gone liquid, and Runtley eases him backward onto a sofa littered with newspapers. He spends the afternoon sleeping over headlines of the war, news of the flying bomb that has landed on a London suburb, the Nazis' new bird of death, and when he awakens the room is filled with shadows, the last riot of sundown, and the doctor is in a chair nearby, watching him.

"Feeling better?"

Baptiste struggles to sit up and feels an arrow of pain where the brace digs into his ribs. He tells Runtley he feels hungover, asking what was in the shot.

"A simple tranquilizer. God knows you needed one. I've never seen you in such a state. Woman trouble?"

"My personal affairs are none of your business."

"Everything is my business. I am dishonest but I am not a gossip. Tell me, Lieutenant. How many times have you made love in the past month?"

"How many bombs have dropped on London? Is this important information?"

"You'll never heal if you keep this up."

"Tend to my back and not my soul."

"Touchy today, aren't we? I suppose it's your broken heart."

By the time Baptiste can stand, adjust his brace, and cross the room to leave, Runtley is already at his heels, following him across the hall and to the door that leads to the next wing. "Off limits, *amigo*."

Baptiste says he'd like to know why.

"Women in there. You're a man, yes?"

Baptiste says he's looking for someone.

"Aren't we all. Come." He takes Baptiste by the arm and leads him back to the other door. "Your jeep is parked out front. I suggest you get into it and drive to Rockenham. Have a warm supper, a bath, and get into that stony bed of yours."

"I have to see her," Baptiste says. "We have things to tell each other."

"Who?"

"Ariel."

Runtley says he doesn't know any Ariel.

"In the other wing. She has her treatments there."

"What kind of treatments, Lieutenant? Have you any idea? Has she told you?"

"Never. Why?"

"Come back tomorrow, Lieutenant. We'll take some pictures of that spine of yours and assess the damage."

Baptiste finds his keys in his shirt pocket. As he guns the jeep's engine, he casts a long glance toward the clinic and sees a few lights already lit in curtained windows off toward the other wing.

"I came with her today," he says to Runtley, who has followed him out. "I brought her in."

Runtley says, "I don't know what you're talking about."

Baptiste wheels the jeep across the lot, driving over a new garden like an oblivious bomber over a city of tiny plants, grinding them into the mud before he spins back onto the road toward the same dying sun as the night before. Ariel, at her window, sees the taillights melt and vanish. No surprises and no sanctuary; darkness falls like a hammer driving the nail of despair.

Ten days later, snug in his bandage and fit as his treatments will allow, he is recalled to London to receive an assignment. Flying bombs are falling as randomly as stars across the city, but in the six months he's been away the war has taken a turn, and for the first time the end is in sight. The armies have landed on the Continent and are moving eastward. Information and money are needed by the resistance and so Baptiste, like a hundred others, is stowed in the bottom of a Dutch trawler and smuggled back to France on a finance run, two million old francs folded into a *plan* and stuffed up his rectum: gun money, money for informants. Out of habit, he uses the village-idiot routine in Paris and slips up once again, this time in the Latin Quarter, and has to make a run for it, finally losing his pursuers in the métro station at Cité (out with the cravat, off with the mustache, rags torn away to reveal a silk shirt, the butterfly shedding the stinking skin of the worm), and a different train north into Belgium, a truck ride to the coast, another fishing boat, and again a sleepless night.

Through the summer he makes three more runs, each time with money, feeding the resistance from a London pipeline. *Obersturmbahnführers* are machine-gunned on sunlit terraces, train rails are torn away, bridges blown to kingdom come, and as the first V2's begin to rain in on London the armies turn north toward Peenemünde.

On leave in London, he searches for Ariel. Runtley, relenting, does not leave him empty-handed. "She's in the city. I don't know which hospital."

"I thought her treatments were finished."

"They are. Now she has another malady. That's all I can tell you."

London, then. Map in hand, Baptiste tours the city, making his way from Chelsea to Kensington, Saint Stephen's Hospital, the Royal Marsden, Battersea General, up north to National Heart, south again to Middlesex, Bainbridge, Agate Street. He is sent to Brussels on a mercy mission and brings back a stranded runner, then continues his search, ever eastward and bearing south, Great Ormond Street, Moorfields Eye, and Saint Peter's. The first impatient leaves of English autumn are falling and he crosses the rushing Thames to the East End, stating again his name and object: I am Baptiste but she knows me as the Other. All the saddened faces tell him to go elsewhere, until a nurse at Saint Peter's says she thinks she knows the name. "A singer, is she? Lovely voice. Being treated for heroin addiction. Is that the one?"

Baptiste says he isn't sure.

"A living storybook, that one. Stories and stories she's got to tell. And in her condition. You the father?"

Baptiste answers that he doesn't have any children. "Do I look that old?"

"Not *her* father. *The* father. Shut my mouth if you didn't know already."

Saint Jude's is not precisely a hospital but a makeshift collection of bedrooms and offices, a place established to occupy the foreign overflow of unwed mothers, refugees, and allies, from a larger hospital not far away. She is still going by the name of Ariel and when he comes upon her she is propped up in bed, her belly covered with a sheet, her hair brushed back away from her face as though she has been awaiting him, as though he is once again late: the rain, the war. He sits at her side, daring only to hold on to her hand while they talk about the fighting, his healed back, her addiction. She is recovered, she tells him, and she is praying that her recovery will last. They tell her that a relapse will forever be a possibility, something like love the drug of her weakness, you think you are over it but you never truly are. She shares her room with another woman, equally pregnant, who turns on her side, leaving her back to them as if to leave them in privacy, but they know she is listening and they do not care.

He can stay only for an hour or so. The floor nurse is adamant. Ariel is a special case and is not to be disturbed. Whatever words Baptiste has recited to himself are forgotten in the wake of the news. It's fair, he reasons. He would not have wanted to know until now. Ariel says she knew. "A mother and a junkie," she says. "I'm not the woman you thought you loved."

She wants him to go but to come again. After the baby, she tells him. After, when she will be in a better state to see him.

When he mentions marriage, she only says there is time. "I have affairs to arrange. Back home. Let the war end first."

Before leaving, he memorizes the room, the print wallpaper with its inevitable orchids, the functional beds, an oak dresser piled high with fresh linen, a single window looking out on a gray street, a crucifix nailed to the wall. She holds his hands in hers, passing her lips from finger to finger, and as he goes out the door she calls after him, telling him he is shorter without the brace but more handsome as well. They blow kisses across the distance and he is gone.

Time and the sun. Time and the moon. In late September, returning from a Channel-run, he is told of the fire, the V2 that came without announcing itself, no scream, no wail, and landed upon Saint Jude's in the dead of night. There is nothing for him to go back to, not even a gravestone. Wild with grief, he leaps from a taxi and scrambles through still-smoking rubble for evidence, but the hospital has burned to its foundation and the ground corps have removed all but the stone and plaster, slivers and ash. Lifting himself from his knees, Baptiste makes his way to a nearby shelter and scans the list of survivors. She is not among them. A similar list of the dead has been posted and he gives it only a glance and then walks away. Coming to the street, he stops and turns back, this time looking more carefully at the list of the dead. She is not among them. How can this be?

He rips both lists from the wall, seeks out the shelter group leader, and presses them upon him.

"I presume you're looking for someone."

"Her name is Ariel. She was here, at Saint Jude's. I saw her ten days ago but her name isn't on either list."

"Then she hasn't been identified. We cannot assume her to be dead or to have survived."

"Then what?"

"The third list, Lieutenant. There is always a third list, you know."

"What third list?"

"The missing, Lieutenant. Those we have not yet found."

LELA MAAR IS MISSING

NEW YORK

1944

I know how to keep a shut mouth. I don't tell secrets on no one. She said to keep it quiet where she was going and I kept it real quiet for a lot of years. I'm a good friend that way. Tell me your troubles and they won't go no further. And anyway, all's I knew was England to clean out the junk, and England's a pretty big town. I didn't have no address or phone number.

When the news was out that she was disappeared, the stories was outrageous. People was writing from as far away as California to say they'd seen her. She was in a coffee shop in Hollywood, in a clinic in Minnesota, in a whorehouse in Baton Rouge. She had a baby in Venezuela and was living in a straitjacket in Chicago. Rumors piling on rumors, and every one a them made those records sell like never before. That's the lesson of it all: die or disappear and the world will take you in its itchin arms forever. There were stories in the paper and most of them were just gossip, a written-down kind of supposing that went on for a few months, and I was surprised when no one guessed Europe, maybe on account a the war there. Start a house on fire and most of us will run the other way. Not Lela. She'll just walk in the front door and sit down. Like I said, corrupt.

I never knew where Harry went. Lela'd tossed him out sometime before getting on that boat, and if he was looking for her he was doing it on the sly. The shame was when he put out another record with a makeshift band and some no-name singer he found God knows where. It didn't sell, of course, not without Lela. Then I heard Harry went to Chicago to start up fresh and that's the last I heard a him till he was dead. Scratch one composer. Jazz guys come and go but mostly they just go.

I lived my life like always, banging at the light like some crazy moth, and I admit to feeling a weight like heartbreak when I'd think of Lela gone for good. That voice a hers, all diamonds and blades, and that look in her eyes: Come get me. I needed money so bad in those days and thought more than once of selling what I knew to the papers for a good meal and a bottle of something French. Gigs were getting harder to come by and I couldn't play the big-band sound. You know. But I'd always been poor, pocketsful of pennies and the rent to pay, and I thought that if I pointed out where Lela'd gone there'd be hell to pay as well. The cost of her loving black me, is how I figured it. So I stayed home and kept my mouth shut and waited for the lights to switch back on.

Only one time I almost broke the secret. When this anarchist man showed up at my door, hat in hand, beggin hard for the truth. I knew who he was. Lela'd been on and off with him for years. He was a criminal but not all that different from me. I let him in and poured him some whisky in a clean glass and we drank together without talking for a long time. I was pleased by his quiet. His clothes was worn out and full a rain and I could tell he was hurting somewhere that he wasn't going to mention. Just Lela, he was saying. He seemed to know I knew where to find her.

You tell me if I lied or not. I'm holding this secret that I'm sworn to keep and a man says, Tell me. Not just any man but a man who walks up and down his life like he dropped something precious and can't for the life of him find it back. I says to him that I just don't know and he says yes I do, his eyes lookin at mine and goin straight to the heart. So I say I got a promise to keep a shut mouth and then I just wait for him to call me nigger or pull a gun or something. But he only sits there lookin at his shoes. Then I'm lookin at his shoes, too, and I notice they don't match, one's brown and the other black. Mine, too, I got two brown ones but not the same make. I wear what I find and not what I want. I'm looking at his shoes and then at my own and then those shoes are moving, black brown black, and he goes out the door just like that.

IN WHICH PAGE IS TAKEN FOR A RIDE

I keep telling myself that my father is in heaven. Art in heaven, rather. And hallowed be his unknown name. The words don't come so easily anymore, not since the Spaniard showed up with his manila envelope and his threats of evidence. When I looked for him he was nowhere to be found. Now that I've stopped looking he won't go away. What bothers me most is that I believe his story, but what am I supposed to do about it? He's wearing out fast, something of a cheap watch to the look of him, but I need time to think it over.

I try to write a letter on Jane's battered Olympia. The keys stick together and make something less than words; I myself can hardly read what I write. Hours pass and I hear Hunter crying in his sleep. Whatever's in his nightmare is getting mingled with my own. When Jane says come to bed I just wave her off and go on typing. He must read English, the old man. And whatever he has to tell me will wait. First I have some things to get off my chest. Dear Dad, if it's you. You rat. Time is wearing us all too thin.

When I was back there suffering jungle rot and loading wet film into my cameras for yet another round with the death scene, I could almost always cheer myself up with the thought that no father of mine was having to sweat out my ongoing brush with mortality. Those grunts in the field had dads back home who were fretting over every news broadcast. A single bullet could cut the genealogy and that would be that. America was getting populated with sonless fathers, men who hit Topflights into green distances and then walked aimlessly after them, and I could console myself that my father was in heaven where he belonged instead of drifting in a limbo from fairway to fairway.

With the dawn's early light, I tear up the letter and head for the street. Skidding along the edges of Riverside Park, I come upon an old man burning garbage in an empty lot. Milk cartons, newspapers, ruined clothes burning in a black smoke as though ghosts are burning as well. A disgusting mattress, the feathers smoldering and stinking. A pile of wet magazines that won't light no matter how much the old man pokes and scatters the pages. A bare-breasted woman on horseback rises on a page from the flames and is sucked back downward. A comb, a box of letters, a sheet of torn wallpaper, cowboy & Indian print, beat-up and unwanted dolls, the hair catching flame and curling into snakes, the plastic faces puckering and collapsing. Finally the old man drags out an enormous carton of photographs, the snapshot variety, moms and pops at the beach, everybody get together and say cheese, gotcha, nearly all of the photos in black & white and gone grayish from years of exposure and fondling. Images burning to black, some family's entire past.

"Whose is this?" I want to know, and the old man gestures to the brownstone nearest us.

"Old lady died and left all this behind."

Taking the stick away from him, I do a bit of poking myself, pushing the dolls and the snapshots toward the hottest flames, getting a regular bonfire going, until the man snatches the stick away, telling me to watch it. "Fire's gotta burn slow, slow. Don't want to start no conflagration."

He has a point. I keep trying to tell the truth but at the same time I don't want to start a brushfire of confession all around me. So I wander away from the fire and head toward home while the sun climbs up over Long Island and streaks the sidewalks almond and sepia, the photograph of Manhattan emerging from the night's litmus.

As I turn off Riverside toward Jane's apartment, I can see in my mind's eye the station wagon parked in front, the attendant at the wheel. He's come for me and I'm ready to listen. My tongue is trapped in my teeth, so I know I won't be able to interrupt. Still limping, I close the distance, and when the attendant sees me on the street he gets out and opens the back hatch of the station wagon and wheels the old man out. No one can tell me just then that he isn't my father, even if he's made up, even if he's comic book instead of Bible. I won't be messed with anymore. The chair touches concrete and he begins to wheel in my direction. When I think I will panic I don't. That immaculate dream of touching him, of hearing him say my name. Imagine we are nearly face to face when a car glides up the street and stops alongside me. Two men jump out from the back seat and confront me on the sidewalk.

"Your name Page?" one of them asks.

I tell him I can't say for sure. "I was hoping to ask the same question."

"We'd like you to take a ride with us."

I feel like telling him to hold his water but already he's got an arm on me and seems to mean serious business. "We don't have a warrant and don't feel we need one. Just come along."

As I am hustled into the back seat of a waiting car, I remember something else the old Spaniard had mentioned. The name of a saint and the place of my birth. At the same time I realize that time is running out and now I'm in the prison of this moving automobile. They're not going to let me off easily. I know what they want from me but I don't know how to deliver it. That's when I go crazy. Time fucks up everything and it makes things old. One of the men starts hitting me while the other holds my neck in a vise between his arms. Dislodging my left hand, I give one of them a jab with all the hate and ugliness I can muster. He pays me back with exorbitant interest.

When I come to they are discussing what I was screaming at them while they beat me.

"Saint Jude," one of them says. "You know what it means?"

The driver says it might be a code word.

"Or an address," says his partner.

"Or a secret," I tell them. But no one is listening anymore.

ACTS OF CONTRITION

They've been holding me for an hour and the room is getting hot, probably an interrogation gimmick, since the place was comfortable enough when I first arrived. There are three of them on the other side of the table, two guys in uniform, officers, and in the middle an old dude in a gray suit with a skinny red tie, eyeglasses that he keeps balanced on the tip of his nose, badly shaven, teeth that need brushing. I assume he has bad breath but am not close enough to tell. He says his name is Randall and he is interested in security. "Containment. Delimitation. My own terms for the surveillance of disinformation. Do you understand me?"

"Of course not."

"You will." He holds some yellow sheets of paper with typing on them and asks questions that sound too prepared to be serious. "We have a good deal of data about you," he continues. "Data being distillation of truth, of course. Will you tell us the truth, Mr. Page?" The other two men just stare at me as if to keep me nailed to my chair. No chance of going anywhere, not with a Marine sergeant standing at the door, sidearm snapped to his shiny black belt.

"The, uh, truth."

"A little color to fill in the blanks in our data."

I know all about military data. Army statisticians will tell you that if you have one foot in the fire and the other in the freezer you must be comfortable. On the average, of course.

"What can you tell us, Mr. Page?"

They've got a file on me at least five inches thick, and *I* don't even know that much about myself, so I'm wondering where they've come up with all this. There are photocopies of my last press card, my flying pass, reports from various COs throughout Vietnam, a birth certificate, a transcript from Columbia, and more yellow and blue pages. I flash for a moment that maybe it's mostly bullshit, filler, just stacks of anything to impress me. But Randall has something else, too, a briefcase full of black & whites that he can only have gotten from Gabriel.

I decide to ask Randall if I can smoke.

"Be my guest."

So I fish a joint from my shirt pocket, a long thin one I've been saving for hours, but Randall says, "Sergeant, take that away from him."

The Marine steps from his place at the door, snatches away the joint, and puts it into his *own* shirt pocket. I can only wonder why no one is smiling. Taking a cigarette from a fresh pack, I can't find any matches, so the sergeant steps forward again, one two, and flashes his lighter, a gold number with the Marine insignia, globe and anchor, *semper fi*, on the cap.

I have always had a soft spot in my hard heart for the Marines. They were the best grunts in Nam, America's finest and, over there, America's deadest. I knew this one Marine named Arthur something who was there because he believed it was his duty, maybe even his destiny. While the grunts were panting through the bush looking to kill, Arthur was right alongside them, forever trying to keep everybody alive. He wasn't very tall and had trouble seeing over the high grass, but he still walked point most of the time, because that's what leaders did. For a lieutenant, he wasn't your usual brownbar, and even the most cynical fucked-up druggie of a grunt could appreciate that. Arthur was the salt of America, and when he wasn't up north in some hellhole he was back around Danang or somewhere setting up a hospital or an orphanage, convinced we had to give something back to the people we were fighting for and against, even if it was only a case of Sam's best Band-Aids. He was for real, this lieutenant, what all the moms and dads back home were thinking of when they thought of the struggle against communism. And as sick as we all got over what we were seeing, we could never hold it against Arthur just because he *believed*. Not to say he was a flag-waver. He simply wanted to save the whole world instead of just his own Caucasian ass. I don't have a single picture of the lieutenant, not even in a group photo. The lens was just too fucking small. All the same, I can remember his face, those ordinary brown eyes and the nose that said he was European, and all the time this little enigmatic nunlike smile that said it was hopeless but he was still hoping. Arthur survived Khe Sanh and then asked for yet another go-round and about a year later I heard he was killed in an ambush while evacuating a village not far from Cam Ranh Bay. I never heard any of the details but this kind of news always traveled the same oral network. "Arthur? Yeah, I heard he got hit." Fire from the trees leaving one man dead. One outrageous jewel of a beating heart of a man. I was in another firefight not long after hearing the news and I was taking a long time getting over it. Me or another grunt, that was one thing, but now America's best blood was getting wasted, not just the blood of criminals and drafted riffraff. Any spark of faith I had left in my country was practically extinguished right there, sometime during that firefight over I don't know what hillside. We won the battle with a napalm strike, and when it was over I took a tab of acid just to get far, far away, then sat down next to a burning tree and took a roll of frames of the burning, in his memory.

"Do you know," Randall is saying, "what this file is telling us?"

"Is this a court of inquiry?"

"A simple interview, Mr. Page."

"Then why do I feel like I'm under arrest?"

Randall isn't listening. He is already deep into his speech. "There are reports and opinions, a psychological profile from an army shrink, a commendation from a platoon sergeant, and of course all of these pictures. We call it evidence, Mr. Page. Evidence of something not quite right. There's a word for a man like you."

"POW?"

"No. Maggot."

I know the word. Any noncombatant who spends six out of seven years in a war zone taking pictures gets used to words like that. Snake's eyes, vulture, buzzard, aphid; carrion and shit-eater, any image along those lines. Something made up, no doubt, by some literate colonel back in Saigon, pissed off at the UPI for printing that picture of the burning village, the story about My Lai, any looking homeward or over the shoulder with doubt. Men who were men had blood on their hands, not ink, and it wasn't any surprise that the Associated Press wasn't winning many Purple Hearts. I myself had run up against various kinds of military resistance, but there was always a chopper heading into the fire, and when things got hot no one really knew the difference, one photographer more or less, another journalist from somewhere, everyone wore green and the jungle, too, was green. Deeply green.

Randall is silent and I just go on smoking, waiting for the other shoe to drop. He picks up a yellow sheet of paper. "Left Columbia spring of 1965, no degree. Assigned as stringer to UPI, July '65, shipped to Saigon one month later. Resigned UPI in January '66 and received free-lance press card after six official refusals. Attached to Third Marines June through December 1966, alternating between northern front and Khe Sanh. Evacuated by military order to Saigon in August of same year and confined to civilian quarters for period of ten days. Left Vietnam during winter of 1966–67, returned some weeks prior to Tet Offensive. Press pass revoked in December of 1968 . . ."

"Stolen."

"What's that?"

"My press pass was stolen."

"It says here . . ."

"Some captain got shook when he saw me taking pictures during a firefight. He was having a bad day, taking caps from all directions. Air cover was slow in showing up and so he took it out on me. Stuck his pistol up my nose and said to hand over my pass. I did."

Randall says he doesn't have the details. "*Revoked*, in any case, is the proper term." Settling his papers, he continues: "Ejected stateside on January 6, 1969, whereabouts undetermined from that time through 1971. Collection of photos published illegally in spring of 1971."

"Illegally?" This is news to me.

"You may be famous, Mr. Page, but you were never given clearance."

There is the unmistakable air of an *ahem* in his voice. *Clearance*, to such a man, having meaning beyond what's in the dictionary. I'm beginning to feel sick. Back to dog images and the penultimate wish to bark.

Randall drones on, "Press card granted under English title, *Starkers*, in December of 1971, returned to Vietnam immediately. Note: trade publication dealing in photos of bare-breasted women; publication folded prior to official release of press pass. Subject wounded in mine explosion March 1974. Two months at Saint-François d'Assise, Saigon; two months U.S. Naval, Honolulu. Wounds fully healed."

"It says that?"

Randall taps a pencil to his folder. "Right here. 'Wounds fully healed.' "

I whistle.

"Earlier in your career you were a standard photographer, a professional, if the term may be applied. Your pictures were sold to Time/Life, to the UPI and the AP, as well as to a number of foreign publications. Then in 1968 or thereabouts your career seems to have taken a sharp downturn. We have nothing precise upon which to base this conclusion, but by all evidence your work was systematically refused by nearly every agency with which you'd previously had contact. Can you explain this?"

"In words?"

"Gestures are permitted but may not necessarily be recorded."

It was a question of style if not of substance. Until 1968, I'd done the usual portraits of soldiers, quick shots of battle sequences, rice paddies, hamlets, orphans. These had been the typical frames of warfare with an eye toward page 1, like the picture that guy Adams took of the man holding a pistol to another man's head and the news saying later that the man had really pulled the trigger. Adams took a lot of hell over that picture, mostly from people asking him why he didn't *do* something. God, as if taking that picture wasn't enough; standing, raising, firing at death from life. I was looking for that same immediacy, an up-to-the-second photography that meant news, yes, but also meant to tell the folks back home what the war was all about. That's what most of us did and it didn't seem to work. Either we weren't getting the right shots or there was some kind of mass myopia going on back at the world. We thought we were all telling you something, that with our visual evidence in your hands no one would be talking up the big game of it anymore. We had the napalm and they had shovels. We didn't have a prayer.

"Mr. Page, would you answer the question, please?"

Then we saw a few hundred thousand more Americans showing up, new camps being built, the jungle being plowed back to make room for something more than the road show it had been up to this point. All that rock and roll was coming off the C-47's and the grunts were all carrying those little automatic cameras, being like us as much as they could, getting enough pictures because no amount of words was going to tell it. So I went a little crazy; or grew sane. You decide. I started to photograph bodies only, spending endless rolls on whatever I could find in the bush, Marine or VC or NVA or any peasants who couldn't get out of harm's way. That's when the news agencies eased up on the paychecks. When I started stuffing manila envelopes like body bags and shipping off these five-by-sevens through Hong Kong so they wouldn't get censored. I stored my negatives in a bank in Saigon but one time some colonel got to them and as far as I know they were destroyed.

"Mr. Page?"

"I lost my touch."

"Your touch? Do you mean you were working poorly?"

"I didn't have what they wanted anymore. I guess I was getting too abstract."

But the dying was not an abstraction. The fine hard gravity of it kept me there, magnetized, my lens melting from more than simple tears. I wanted the entire universe revealed to me and was praying that it would prove to be something more than atomic combinations, spirals of DNA, Hare Krishnas, or sorceries. I turned away from bodies, bullet holes, open wounds, and began shooting geometries, gray on black, jungle horizons, aerial views of rice paddies like a matrix of skin. A pile of human hair burning in a campfire. That severed hand grasping a stone. Of course, I couldn't sell a single frame of it to any of the usual magazines. I didn't want to. The pictures weren't for mass publication. I didn't take any more photographs with people in them, and that left everyone disappointed. As long as they thought of me as some kind of historian, saving those images for later use, justification, glorification, or identification, I was acceptable. But when the war, their war, became my own personal dark room, that was another matter. Kids in the villages used to gather around and plead with me to take their pictures, and all I could tell them was *Didi mao*, fuck off, I just didn't have it in me anymore. I couldn't look at some doomed baby and close my finger over that shutter. The gig had become truly sick or worse sometime between my stay at the mission and the time I got to know Dune Buggy, and I should have gotten out right then. A photographer who can't take pictures of people, not who won't but who *can't*, must be in a pretty bad way. The night I met Dune Buggy, he looked at some of my stuff and told me I'd gone to hell.

One of the officers passes a manila folder to Randall. Opening it, the old man takes out a picture and holds it up to me. "Is this one of yours?"

I recognize it immediately. "That's Dune Buggy."

"David Ambrose, E-6."

"We had alternate names. Usually on our helmets."

"I know the custom. Mr. Ambrose was the father of the child you are adopting, was he not?"

Here we go. What the moment is demanding is a masterpiece of mythology, a gloriously spun yarn. "The baby," I answer, "was his and Chulin's."

"Did you take this picture?"

"I must have." We were at a cathouse on a Saigon back street. One of those weeks before we knew Chulin. Dune Buggy, who never shot up, was up to the eyeballs with horse. We'd seen a lot of dead people through the previous ten days, most of them American. That night, drinking wouldn't get us past it, nor marijuana, nor getting laid in the shade.

Where'd you get the needle, Dune Buggy?

From a chick.

What chick? A round-eye?

Just a chick.

Randall asks me if I am aware of the child's status at the moment. "He is in your custody, but until the adoption goes through he remains a ward of the state. The military maintains absolute authority."

I nod, although everything in my being is shaking insanely.

"As it happens, we have other things to ask you about. Beginning with this." He holds the photograph of a black man with a string of shriveled ears around his neck, those VC ears you had to have to be a hard ass, a pro's pro. The label on the helmet reads *High Priest* and he is wearing an M-79 grenade launcher over his right shoulder.

I say that I knew the guy.

"You were in action together?"

I can feel the ring of menace growing smaller and tighter. "Only once."

"Care to tell us about it?"

"Why bother? You probably already know."

Randall lights a cigarette of his own, his first during the interrogation. "We know that he was in business for himself. We know that he actually *liked* the killing."

"A lot of grunts could fit that description."

"Might we not call them soldiers?"

"Behind the lines they were soldiers. When it got hot they were grunts. They had their own way of putting things."

"Tell us about High Priest."

They call it the Look. Most short-timers have it, those with only a month or two to go. When everything you've seen has done a number on the pupils, messed up the cornea, or shifted the retina to slightly off-center. Usually you get the Look after your first real firefight but sometimes it takes longer. It comes over you when puking doesn't help, or screaming, or crying. When crying would be a fine thing to do if only you could manage the tears. High Priest was past the Look. He had something in his eyes I'd never seen before. We all had those sundowns to some extent, whites of the eyes blown full-time scarlet from lack of sleep and fear pumping the blood day and night. Most of the killers had it in a way that could be broken down into types: crazed, drained, drugged, or terrorized. High Priest was serene but his was a terrible-looking serenity.

"I followed a patrol up north and we were getting sniped at by some of the best. Definitely not the VC. These guys had their aim down to a science. By the time we got from one village to the next we had six KIA and two wounded. One guy was screaming all the way up the trail but we didn't have any morphine to give him, because the boys had snorted it all up the night before back at the bunker. Everybody was clean and hot. You know, jumpy. The village was nice and quiet but we'd seen places like it before. A few hooches with rice paddies on four sides, a pig pen, nothing but old ladies and little kids. The women looking dirty at us when we came in. Nothing out of the ordinary. The CO tossed a couple of families out of their shacks and told us to move in. Nobody knew where High Priest was and I don't think anybody cared, we were that tired."

"Was this day or night?" Randall asks.

"Evening or late afternoon."

"Were you in contact with anyone? Was there a radio?"

"You'd have to ask the CO."

"Why do you say that when you know he's dead?"

"Black humor."

One of the officers writes something on a sheet of paper in front of him. Or he is only pretending to write—intimidation by documentation? We know all about you, Page. You maggot.

"Tell us the rest."

"Sometime during the night we had incoming. At least that's what we thought at first. It was funny, because after a while you get to know the sounds of friendly fire as opposed to *their* fire and this time it seemed we were getting hit with friendly mortar rounds, one every thirty seconds or so. It was from close in but we didn't know how close. One hooch after another was going down, every one but the two we were camped in. About half an hour later, High Priest came strolling into the village like he had just gone out for some air. By that time most of us had already figured it was him."

"How?"

"The mortars. Those were M-79 shells, and High Priest had the only M-79 on the block."

"Why do you suppose he was shelling his own men?"

"He wasn't shelling us, just the rest of the village."

"Have you any idea why?"

"Sure. All that rice we saw coming in."

"Rice?"

"It was late afternoon or early evening when we got there. We saw about a dozen people around, maybe fifteen, no men at all. There were about ten huts in that village and so few people."

"What about the rice, Mr. Page?"

"There was a mountain of it. Enough to feed at least fifty. Rice doesn't last all that long once it's been cooked and we knew they hadn't steamed it up just for us. That meant VC. It wasn't all that hard to figure out. Anyway, it wasn't the first village we'd ever been in."

"So you all assumed that the village was controlled by the Viet Cong?"

"We were sure of it."

"And High Priest decided to do something about it."

"That's right."

"Was he under orders from his commanding officer?"

"No one in that outfit was under orders of any kind. It was a search-and-destroy and most of the boys were in business for themselves."

"Then the commanding officer had nothing to do with the mortar attack?"

"He was against it. Promised to bring charges against High Priest."

"What were you doing at the time?"

"Loading my camera."

"Did you take any pictures that night?"

"A few."

Randall flips through his files and comes up with an enlarged version of the same picture of High Priest. "Can you identify the man in this picture?"

"I told you. High Priest."

"I mean this other man."

His finger is pointing to a body at High Priest's feet. Mud-caked bars on the shoulder, a clean bullet hole the size of a pencil between the eyes.

I told him that would be the CO.

Randall drags out more paper. "In December of 1969, charges were brought against Charles Lee Simpson, E-1, known to his platoon as High Priest. He was charged with having murdered his commanding officer on the night of November 16, 1969, while on a search-and-destroy. We are speaking of the same night, I believe."

"It was the same night. We didn't have any calendars along, but I'll take your word for it."

"And you admit to having taken this picture?"

I tell him there's no mistaking the style. Black and white, just off the distance needle, and a flimsy green filter.

"Then you must know how the CO was killed."

I tell him I was there.

"You mean you were a witness?"

I repeat that I was there.

Randall lifts the photograph to his eyes as though to give it another look-see, then drops it to the table. "Did you know that a member of that CO's family found this picture in a book? Your book, published in 1971. The officer's grieving father. Can you imagine his feelings upon seeing this photograph? His sorrow and his rage?"

I tell him I can imagine.

"Were you aware that charges were brought against Charles Lee Simpson?"

"Who?"

"High Priest."

"I heard about it, yes."

"And yet you withheld evidence. You offered no testimony."

I answer that I didn't withhold anything. "I was there. I took the picture. You have the picture in your hands and probably copies of it elsewhere, in the basement. That's testimony enough."

"Can you explain why you weren't questioned? Why all the others in that village were interrogated but not you?"

"I was moonlighting."

"Please explain the term."

"No one officially knew I was there. I was just along for the ride, nothing more. Like a stowaway."

"When you heard about the charges, why didn't you come forward?"

I can see where we're heading. We're moving up the river into a cross-fire. Flares light the way for us, rising whoosh into the night sky and falling hissing to the water. They want my guilt and they're ready to reach deep for it, elbows deep into my own personal shithole. Trying to get to the soul of me with facts and statistics. The dog is gnawing at my feet and wants blood.

"I followed the investigation. I had nothing to add to it."

"Simpson was acquitted."

"Acquitted and discharged," I remember. "He wasn't all there anymore."

"But he wasn't innocent, was he?"

"No one is innocent."

"A philosophical point, Mr. Page?"

"The CO died. He was fighting a war and he went under."

"Did you see him die?"

"Yes."

"Did Simpson shoot him?"

"Yes."

"Are you certain?"

"Yes."

Randall sits back in his chair, his glasses still balanced at the end of his nose, his red tie now pulled down low, his top button undone, collar loosened. Down to brass tacks. Cards on the table. Up front. On the line. He holds the photograph between thumb and forefinger and I realize I'm forgetting something crucial, like that joke about the dog who keeps shitting on the floor. Every time he does it, they put his nose in it and then throw him out the window. He persists. But one day he learns. He shits on the carpet, sticks his *own* nose in it, and then jumps out the window. A kind of learning I'm usually prone to.

"Did you take this picture, Mr. Page?"

"I've already said that I did."

"When you took this picture, would you say that you were against the war?"

"No."

"Then you were *for* the war?"

"No."

"Which was it, Mr. Page? For or against?"

I know the answer, have always known it. "Neither. I was watching."

"Watching what, Mr. Page?"

"The war. All of it. There was a lot to see."

"Is that why they called you Wide Eyes?"

"No."

"Then how did you get your nickname?"

"Because of a story I once told."

They are all waiting, all three of them—four, if you count the Marine at the door. Waiting to hear my story.

"I don't remember when or where. I'd been there about a year, maybe less."

Randall checks his records. "In Saigon?"

"No, someplace else. Danang maybe. I was telling about how you couldn't close your eyes there. You could sleep but you couldn't close your eyes. Something in the war reminded me of a woman I had once seen in Marseille. She didn't have any eyelids."

"So they called you Wide Eyes. Was that the tag on your helmet?"

"I never really had a helmet of my own. I kept losing them. Somebody always came up with one for me."

"And you took this picture?"

The same one. I nod.

"With a Leica."

"No. A Canon. Night film in black and white with a bottle-green filter. Bad distance setting. That's my weakness, keeping my distance."

"So you witnessed a murder and took a picture of the killer and victim. You kept the picture, even published the picture, but you didn't turn in the killer. What does that make you, Mr. Page?"

"A photographer from Vietnam."

"It makes you an accessory in a court of law."

"If you say so."

"Our opinion of you is very low, Mr. Page."

They want war and they want law. Having it both ways and insisting that they are one and the same. I once saw a grunt cover a baby with Band-Aids and in the next village blow away an old lady out of simple frustration. In the most criminal of wars, someone was always looking for a killer to walk point. Go out on search-and-destroy to get a body count and don't come home without double digits. Hunting with a full magazine, you shot water buffalo, pigs, birds, gooks. Then you went home, shaved, got drunk, listened to the radio, died a little death, and were glad it wasn't *death* death. They wanted law and you filled up body bags with something resembling men. I filled a thousand rolls of film and every one of those frames shot through my eyeball and landed indelibly on the floor of my heart. What was left of my heart. Stained glass that wouldn't come clean. I never shot anyone with bullets, never even fired a gun. The lords up north, the grunts with necklaces of human ears, jungle-rotted for a year or so and then went home to become firebugs or worse. I stayed. And kept my eyes open. I couldn't tear myself away from the beauty of hell, that shade of green. At the hospital where I spent some time, there was an amputee, a dude with no legs, who used to wheel over to a blind guy and spoon him up his soup. The blind guy said he wasn't blind, he still saw the color red, saw it clearly even though he didn't have any eyeballs, just these two black sockets that nobody could look at without feeling uneasy. Nurse Nurse used to go behind the screen to cry sometimes and that always soothed me, the sound of a woman crying, and now and then I wished she would come and cry all over me, just so I could feel her tears falling on my face.

I had sent a collection of my corpse photos to *The New York Times* but never saw any of them in print. A letter came back asking me not to contact them in the future, not now, not ever. Another batch went to *Life* magazine but they weren't in the market for black and whites, they said. To *Time*, to *Newsweek*, to the *U.S. News & World Report*. Evidence, I told them. Pornography, they replied. When I needed press credentials, *Starkers* came through for me, a skin magazine for men who liked big lolos and pictures of Mom. Gabriel found art publishers who printed my photographs without text or captions, and people said it was an antiwar collection, anti-Vietnam or anti-America. For a few weeks I was invited to dinner parties, SDS meetings, lectures, and discussion groups, and felt something being peeled away from me even as I sat in an alcoholic stupor before baying hounds, slapdash poets, activists of every stripe, having become that lowest of the era's creatures, a spokesman for my generation. Jane took me to her bed and later to her heart but I couldn't live with myself anymore so I went back, knowing there were always more pictures where the others had come from. The century was rife with them, frames of incredibility, evidence, memory, and all I had to do was what anyone could have done, a simple enough gesture, normal, natural, effortless, rare. I only had to open my eyes.

The papers are back in their file. Paper clips and staples restored and fastened, the photographs sifted and stacked and folded away. Their history binds me hand and foot with my own rope. Because I didn't blink.

Randall lights a cigarette and blows blue smoke toward the ceiling. I am free to go, he tells me. This is not a court of law. "I'm an investigator, not a judge." All the same, he has a report to file, and Hunter will be lost to me. Consider this: I am unfit to be a father.

"What will you do with him?"

"I imagine he will be returned to where he came from."

"To Vietnam?"

"Yes. To that mission, if it's still there."

I would find him alone in a nameless alley. I would tear out his windpipe and feed it to the same dog that was feeding on me. Momentarily without time and place, I have to hurry. I get as far as his table but the Marine has me before I can do any violence. Everyone is dying anyway and there's no one left to kill. I am led into the hallway and out to a waiting black car. By the time I get home, Hunter is already gone and Jane is in bed, weeping into feathers.

The night is long and without language. I sleep and awaken with fresh grief. Jane holds me and then releases me. When the sun comes up, I rise to close the curtains and hold the darkness in. There is no rain and no sunlight, no weather at all. We move about the room, obsessed with the walls, and from time to time we collapse into each other and tear at each other's skin.

On the second day of this, morning or evening, I can hear the siren, the doorbell like a mosquito hum, long and insistent. Jane can't manage it and I go alone.

It is the old Spaniard's attendant. There is rain in his hair and I remember who I am.

"He's dead," he tells me.

I had guessed as much.

"They buried him this morning up in the Bronx. I can give you directions but there isn't much to see."

He's holding that manila envelope in his dirty hands and I ask him if it's for me.

He hands it over. "Nothing much in it. Just a passport."

I take it from the envelope and open it. Santos Grace. Born September 19, 1914.

"He said it belongs to you."

This doesn't make sense but I nod all the same.

"He said he stole it. That's how he came to America."

"What else did he say?"

"Before his heart went, he was hurting all the time. Pain and all. He was sick for a long time and didn't know how to find you until he saw your book."

"My photography?"

"How should I know? Your book, he said."

The birthdate is the same as my own: September 19. He said his name was Grace but he'd once been Baptiste. "Where'd he say he stole the passport?"

"In Paris. Listen." The attendant holds out his hand, palm up. "You got cabfare for me? I had a long drive in just to give you that."

When he's gone I sit in the middle of the living room, opening and closing the passport like a trap door that gives into darkness. Jane goes into the bathroom and closes the door. There is weather again, rain slanting against the window, and night arrives on a ruinous wind. There is a burning of dead leaves and old letters in my chest. The archives at the pyre. Jane comes from the bathroom and puts her arms around me, telling me we have to find him, our child. I'll have to find him and bring him back. I try telling myself that not everything is lost but it's no go. The dog is barking and there is nothing more to feed him.

AT THE SAINT LAZARUS STATION

PARIS

1947

He is asleep before his seed has dried along her leg. His breathing is as even and as shallow as a child's, and when he turns his back to her she can hear him no longer, and except for his fingerprints on her face and breasts and that trickle of cooled sperm she can believe that he isn't in her bed and that she hasn't again collaborated with life, or whatever of life her means of survival will permit.

The windows are open to the summer night and she can hear a trio of drunks arguing as they make their way along the rue Ballu in the ninth *arrondissement* of Paris. By their accents, they are from the Midi, possibly soldiers on leave, on their way back from a brawl at the Place de Clichy, their pockets empty and the subway closed for the night. It is a long walk to the barracks south of Montparnasse and the taxis are for American soldiers, not French.

The diplomat, Page, rolls onto his stomach, his face turned away from hers, and she lifts the sheet, rising from the bed to stand naked at the window, where a breeze cools her arms and legs. She stands just beyond the light, in a shadow where the men will not see her if they happen to look the three stories upward. They are not soldiers, they are vagabonds, *clodos*, ex-resistance perhaps; three years after the fighting there are so many of them still living underground, remembering and adding up old debts, passing messages to each other under tables and across latrine walls. . . . *The city is ours*. They are arguing over money, the cost of a train to Deauville, and they disappear at the corner of the rue de Clichy, where a broken streetlamp leaves a patch of blue darkness to enshroud them. Beyond that darkness, she is thinking, there is a man. She has seen him more than once and can only assume that he is following her. The first time she noticed him was at the Parc Monceau. He was wearing a blue work shirt and pretended to read a newspaper, but when she'd left the park he'd followed. She'd seen him twice since, in the street below the apartment, looking upward as though in search of her window. Though she is not convinced it is the same man. One face becomes another so easily nowadays.

All winter long the windows across the street have been closed and shuttered but now, in the irregular heat of June, an early scirocco traversing the Mediterranean and the plain of the Midi, the windows are opened wide, a breeze ululating the gauzy *voilages* of a second-floor window. Looking downward from one floor above them, Nadine can see the couple in their bed, well past midnight, seesawing against each other, the man on his knees behind the woman, whose head is bent to the pillow, her hands gripping the rails of the headboard, Christ on His crucifix above the bed looking on mournfully. Nadine knows the couple. They have only recently been married and just last week moved into the long-empty apartment above the *teinturerie*, hauling suitcases and cartons and chests and heirlooms salvaged from the war up the creaking wooden stairway and putting geraniums along the balcony to relieve the street of its postwar dreariness. A declaration of love and sunlight, these flowers are like crossed fingers against the passage of time.

Someone said that the broad blank wall along the side of the *teinturerie* has been replastered since the liberation. Bullets tore the concrete when the Germans used the wall as a backdrop to execute resistance fighters. "They were communists," Madame Claret has told her, "but there should be a monument because they were Frenchmen all the same." But the city, her husband reminds her, is already crowded with monuments; stone and bronze and marble are everywhere, icons to the noble dead. "Anyway, there's the church not far from here, the Trinité. Go there and remember. And light a candle for the living."

The son of the owner of the *teinturerie* is named Philippe and because he is a homosexual he had been suspected of sleeping with the German soldiers. Something unhealthy in that logic: fearing above all else men who love men. All enemies are perverse and the perverse are our enemies. Philippe is said to have done the plastering, filling in the bullet holes and then whitewashing the whole wall. One story up is where the young couple has put out flowers, and Nadine, standing naked before the window, thinks that it is all a plastering over, this hurried redecorating of the vast European theater, dabbing perfume here and there to cover the smell. But that smell is stronger than any perfume, and the bloodstains seep through the wallpaper; weeds will grow in the cracks of the floorboards and children will find disassembled bones in the cellar.

Nadine shivers, watching the man buckle and come and withdraw from his wife, who kneels trembling, her buttocks yellow in the lamplight. So different, their coupling, from hers and Page's. The American is hurried and ungenerous, as though he has a train to catch. Once, moved by memory if not the diplomat, she hooked her legs around his and leaped to meet his thrust and afterward he had been startled by her tears, asking over and over what he'd done, what on earth had he done. She learns not to remember anything when he is inside of her, doing instead as a whore once recommended to her, memorizing the ceiling, the map of its near country, cracked and rivered and peeling of mountains, in the sky above the bed.

Mrs. Page resides in New York but the diplomat, on temporary assignment to France, has brought along the boy and hired Nadine to care for him as well as the apartment. There is no contract, only her weekly salary, in small bills, left in an envelope on the kitchen table each

Saturday. Nowhere is it written, except in her understanding of such arrangements, that he will nightly visit her bed. That she cannot have children is to his advantage, and she often wonders how he arrived upon a price for her, the occasional sum of fifty thousand francs, once she began opening her legs to him. She wonders as well if his government foots the bill and if he has to fill out a voucher for it, a two-line entry, one line for *femme de ménage* and the other line marked simply *femme*.

She would leave him, would already have left him, if he had not brought along the boy. Now almost three years old, the child had arrived in Paris blind, a victim of shock and perhaps a wound that had never been found. She had taken him into her heart immediately, caring for him and for the diplomat with a single-mindedness that overshadowed her loathing of the long nights in the hired bed. She had been a simple whore and now she was a mother. She read stories to the boy in French, and though he could barely understand the words he seemed to know what she was saying and asked again and again for the same story, "*Le Canard Vilain*," and she was touched that he should prefer a fable of sorrow and triumph to those of adventure or fantasy or humor. The duck that was a swan. She likened it to her own fable of sadness, that of the mermaid returned to the cold sea, swimming as if against the current of her own life, her hair tangled in the swaying kelp of remembering, remembering. My prince is dead.

On her forehead there is a thin scar that looks from a distance like a half-moon. Each day, rising from her bath, she dries herself and applies her makeup, smearing her forehead with a red cream that rubs down into pink, covering over that scar much as the homosexual covered over the bullet holes on that wall. One night, as she was sleeping alone, she awakened and found the boy standing next to her bed. When she opened her eyes, he frowned and reached a finger to her face. In the half-darkness, she realized he could see her; his eyes were open and he was looking at her, first at her eyes, then her lips, then the rest of her. "Hunter?" she said. And he nodded. "Can you see me?" As if to answer, he reached a finger to her face. She had thought he was going to touch her nose, one of his blind gestures of affection, but his finger rose instead to above her eyes and rested on the scar, the ragged C that had been carved there with a rusty knife by her Montparnasse landlord. A bleeding C, now white and cicatrized. *Collaboratrice*. The boy's first vision had been the evidence of her sin. Ever since that night, she has also applied the cream before going to bed and finds pinkish streaks across her pillow in the morning.

She sees him watching her, still. And in his gaze she imagines there is love, though he never says the word. His mother, he is told, is dead. She was a famous singer and Page is now his father. He pretends to understand and hangs close to the diplomat whenever they are in the same room. He is sometimes afraid of Nadine now; he hides from that scar. When he was blind, he held her more tightly.

The couple across the way lie in each other's arms, heads resting on stacked pillows. They pass a cigarette back and forth and then the husband turns out the light and Nadine can see only the cigarette moving from left to right, right to left, in the darkness.

She keeps her valise under her bed and it is already packed, her things neatly folded and arranged geometrically, the leather strap pulled tight. René will be waiting for her in a few hours and she will step into his car as into another life and it will be the boy who will lead her there. The diplomat, she is sure, will pay their price and there will be no violence. When he arrives home from the embassy he will find the note and will fulfill its instructions. It is his nature, she tells herself. He may even understand why I am doing this.

A familiar fear wells up in her and she fights to suppress it. Standing before the window, she feels lighter, more hollow than thin, and she imagines herself ascending, ever ascending, as though any minute now she will disappear through the window and it will be too late to reach under the bed for her valise. The diplomat is sleeping there, his heavy body adding a depth to the bed that was never there before. Most nights, though there is no one but the boy to see him, he leaves just before dawn and sleeps the last hour in his own bed, waiting for Nadine to come with his bowl of café au lait and a tartine, when they are strangers anew, diplomat and *femme de ménage*, and she reminds him to call the embassy before leaving and he says, Don't forget to take Hunter to the Parc Monceau, the weather is so much better now and he shouldn't be indoors all the time. Now and then, when the diplomat is alone for dinner, he invites her to sit with him, offers her coffee and cognac, and though his French is atrocious, no attempt on his part to do other than transform the words mechanically, he will draw her into conversation, asking her where she's from and about her family. Her father, she tells him, was originally from Bordeaux but came to Paris after the first war to find work. Her mother died when she was young; she never knew her.

And your father? What was his work?

He was a machinist, at a millinery. He repaired the machines.

Sewing machines?

Yes, she says in English. We were not poor.

Where in Paris did you live?

She says, We lived in Montparnasse.

Where the writers were?

She never knew any writers. She knew only the people on her street, the rue du Maine.

The diplomat is obsessed with the writers. You must at least have heard of them. Miller, Hemingway, Gertrude Stein. And there were painters, too, from all over Europe. You've never heard of Pablo Picasso?

Of course she has. She reminds him that she went to school, she is not just some urchin off the streets.

He apologizes.

Page is from New York, a place that is only hearsay to Nadine. During the war, he was stationed in London supervising Lend Lease shipping across the Baltic Sea. It was there that he had taken in the boy: They said he was American and I suppose it made a difference. It took me two years to trace the identity of his mother. Have you heard of her in France? Until I found out who she was I had no idea she was famous. A strange story. She disappeared in early 1944, maybe earlier, and I could only trace her from London, where she'd been since the beginning of the same summer. The rest is a blank. Somewhere in that blank is Hunter's father.

What will you do if you find him?

I don't know. I've had him nearly three years now and cannot imagine being without him. What would you do?

Give him up.

Could you do that? Just like that?

No.

The previous month he had been assigned to a military branch investigating war criminals. He had been asked to interrogate an SS officer who had given himself up in a farmhouse the previous week. The German had been a secretary to Klaus Barbie and had fled Lyon with his French mistress before the city had been overrun. For three years he had remained hidden in his lover's bedroom, leaving only twice: once for a nervy midnight stroll and the second time in an attempt to get back to Germany. He had been picked up close to Nancy when he'd foolishly entered a café to ask for directions and had been recognized as German.

"There were two crimes involved," the diplomat had explained to Nadine. "His own past complicity in the exportation of French Jews, and the crime of his mistress for having hidden him." He had begun to describe the townspeople's reactions when her hand, like a vise upon his arm, stopped him short.

"I know the story," she had told him.

"But you couldn't know it. It just happened."

She answered that of course she knew the story. "All of France knows the story. Doesn't America?"

Taking the boy for ransom had been René's idea but she admits to herself that the guilt will be hers. Time is to her like a book torn in two, before the war and after, and what she can read of herself makes no sense. What matters now is to get out of France, the flowered mausoleum of a war that no one, after all, has won. Not in France. When the rapist is dead you have still been raped. This is René's logic, though she reminds him that she loved a *good* German and wears this scar in his memory. René only shrugs. He is a mercenary now, her heroic cousin who fought with the resistance and at the end of the war found himself at the end of a long line of anonymous men in dirty clothes begging for bread. Once he was a poet and now he is a criminal, a thief. Stealing from his countrymen is his greatest pleasure, but he also enjoys extorting the American, who he is sure will pay up "as long as we aren't greedy. Enough to get out is all. He will see we are reasonable and will answer us in kind."

She will find another country, a new language, an alien culture that will house her grief. Years will pass and the scar will grow pale and be taken for a half-moon, an ornament and a symbol of love rather than betrayal.

His mother was French. She repeats the words to herself, before the open window. *Sa mère était française.* The one branch of the family tree that might have shaded him from their wrath. But if we hadn't won the war there would have been no crime. Love would simply have been love. Or if he'd fled with the army, gone back to the other side of the Rhine, she might later have rejoined him in Bonn or in Frankfurt. His family was from Cologne, Köln in German, a city so ambiguous in its history as to have once been neither French nor German. A city of collaborators, kingless in two languages.

Night, all the night, will not cover her, and she feels as though she will never again sleep. Her eyes still burn from the sight of the lovers sweating one against the other. They must be sleeping now, the man's leg hooked over the woman's, binding her to the bed. She watches their window to see if they might stir anew and feels an immediate shame. Loveless, I watch love. It's an easy pastime for a widow. She turns and makes certain that the diplomat is still asleep, then steps closer to the window, where she can feel a thin breeze, and she raises her arms to cool them.

His name was Jürgen, and after a few months of meeting secretly they'd found a priest, a communist from Alsace-Lorraine, to marry them. The wedding had been held in the cellar of the church, without witnesses, a week before the liberation of Paris. Jürgen had worn one of Nadine's father's shirts and the blue wool trousers of his uniform. The priest had said, "Be neither Nazi nor Vichy nor fascist nor democrat," and Jürgen had laughed before he could finish, and Nadine had always wondered what it was the priest might have bade them be. Jürgen wrote a short letter to his father to explain that he would not be home with the others, then went into hiding in Nadine's small apartment on the rue du Maine, where they spent endless days in the confinement of each other's arms, hearing the fighting outside while Nadine repeated French phrases over and over so that Jürgen could learn to say them without accent. Once an American captain had visited her landlord with a paper saying that he had a right to search the building. Jürgen had hidden under the bed, and when the captain had come to her door, she had opened to him and thrown her arms around his neck crying, *Vive l'Amérique*, as she'd seen the other French girls do. The captain had been charmed. Giving her a quick kiss and feel, he'd only glanced around the room, then left. Jürgen, coming out from under the bed, had been wet with fear and shame. The war will never end. I will give myself up to them.

She hears the boy crying in his sleep and reaches across the bed for her nightgown. His room is down a narrow hallway, toward the back of the apartment, where the night's traffic will not disturb his already fragile sleep. When she arrives, he is waiting for her, sitting up in his bed, his arms outstretched. His lamp has been turned off. The diplomat, passing from her room to his own, always steps in to turn it off once the boy is asleep. There are worse things to fear than the dark, he says. Nadine answers, "Are there?"

She brings the boy a glass of water. He spills a bit down his pajama front and she dries him with her fingers, then brushes the hair from his eyes and kisses his forehead. He reaches a finger and traces it along her scar, then asks her if it hurts. No, she tells him. It used to hurt but it doesn't anymore.

He falls asleep without asking her to light the lamp so she opens his curtains to let in the glow of the city. Since the room is warm she opens the window as well. In the morning Page will be angry, but she doesn't care. He will be angrier still when he returns home to find her letter.

As she is leaving the room, she notices the passport. It is atop the boy's dresser, half hidden by a book of fables. She opens it and reads his name, the date and place of birth. She remembers René telling her that since the war's end an American passport is priceless. It is the fastest way out of the wasteland, and the pickpockets at Pigalle are more interested in passports than in dollars. A good forger, according to René, can convert an American passport and sell it to anyone for a fantastic sum.

It is nearly dawn and she can hear the diplomat in the hallway. He is making his way through the darkness to his own bed. Reaching a hand inside her gown, she clutches the passport to her breast and then steps into the hall. When he sees her, he acts more embarrassed by his nakedness than he normally would be in daylight. "Is something wrong?" he asks.

"No," she answers. "A nightmare. Since he can see, he has them every night. I opened his window."

"Fine," he answers, then turns toward his own door. "Please wake me in an hour. I have an early appointment."

Alone in her bed, she watches the light change beyond her window, an almost chemical transformation, the ink-black sky slowly becoming the color of a bruise. On the rue du Maine she knew an artist, Alain, who worked as a forger for the resistance. When they cut her hair and marched her through the streets of Montparnasse with the other collaborators, Alain defended her with his fists and took a beating for it. Later, unable to find work, he went off to live with his family in Pontoise. She has not seen him in nearly three years and assumes he has given up his art for honest labor.

Her valise is packed, the strap pulled tight. All of her possessions. All of her hopeless underthings, mended skirts, *chemisiers* frayed to translucence, one whispering lone stocking she cannot wear for want of the other. It is only dawn and already the day is uncommonly warm. She rises before the sunlight enters her window and goes into the bathroom, taking out her makeup while the bathwater is still running. All of her cream has come off in the night and the scar appears blue against her pale forehead.

She steps in and out of her bath, the water too warm somehow, making her lonesome for something she cannot name. As she dries herself, she gazes into the mirror, then opens her jar of cream and smears two fingers across her forehead. The diplomat never asks her about the wedding ring. Maybe he knows. Maybe he only thinks of her as a whore. Her fingers move in a slow semicircle, tracing and retracing the C until the cream dissolves, scarlet to rose to sepia to the color of her flesh, in the name of the father and of the son.

At sunrise he is watching the window. For a month now he has been watching, following, standing guard against shadows and evil winds. Looking in windows and through doorways, from across the street or any distance; keeping his eyes on his son until night falls and then going back to his black hole to sleep. The candle sputters out and the wind comes up, waking him. He pulls on his trousers and worn boots and tramps the north of Paris to the rue Ballu, and as the sun comes up he takes his place alongside the *teinturerie* and begins his watch.

Time has turned to small change, centimes and coppers, a daily dwindling. He had finished his war and gone back to London to grow old, and there had read of the death of Lela Maar in the London *Times*. It all came back; she died the same death as Ariel and the article says her son survived. He is the ward of Armand Page, American diplomat.

He arrived in Paris without money or plan, nothing to convince himself that the past could be unraveled. At the embassy he inquired as to the whereabouts of A. Page and was given the address on the rue Ballu. After climbing the stairs, he stood before the door a long time without knocking and then went back down those stairs out the door. In a lavatory at the Gare Saint-Lazare he washed his hands and shaved his beard, brushed the dust from his frayed cuffs, and wiped his boots with a wet rag. In the mirror his ugliness filled him with despair, and by the time he arrived again at the rue Ballu Armand Page was just coming home, tie and jacket impeccable, *Le Figaro* under one arm and a briefcase in the other. They crossed paths for a moment, Page's greeting going unanswered. A nodding of strange heads, Baptiste breathless and Page oblivious.

He lives in abandoned buildings, and when he cannot any longer stay away he returns to watch. The accounting is simple enough: he has no money and no evidence. He has taken up with a roving band of bums, trailing along with them across the northern edges of Paris, from Saint-Lazare and the Place de Clichy to beyond Montmartre, the dark side, and below to Pigalle, Anvers, Jaures. If there is work in Paris he's had none of it offered to him, so he makes his living taking pictures of tourists, mostly American soldiers, and when his hunger is unbearable he haunts the more affluent quarters, offering photographs or begging, whichever will work best for him. Now and then he sells his other photographs, those he has taken during lonesome walks in the city. The French love artists if not art, and he will not entirely starve. He is tolerated by the bums because his photographs assure them of their identity. On the street, unshaven and stinking of sneaky pete, they seem invisible, but when Baptiste unwinds his film and in the darkness of a back-alley cellar develops his photos, they wait expectantly outside, not unlike worried fathers, pacing. When he hands over the prints, they pass them from one to another, too astonished at first to comment upon what they see. They laugh nervously and examine their faces with their hands, smoothing over and caressing the whiskers, the sores, the lines of passing time.

But Paris is no longer home. Not with the boy living here. He knows that he will have to leave, that to present his face would be unforgivable, terrible, pointless. The father is the man who cares for him now, not this pale derelict. Soon enough he will have to slip the knot and disappear, and daily he tells himself that the time has come.

So he has arrived this dawn determined that it will be his last day. The sky is white and the sun already hot. The woman will take the boy to the park and Baptiste will vanish into sunlight as into darkness and the watching will be ended.

It is midmorning when he sees the woman coming out the door, one hand bearing a small suitcase and the other holding the boy. From the Place de Clichy they head west along the Boulevard des Batignolles and he realizes they are heading toward the Parc Monceau, which is odd, since, in a month of following them, he has never seen them visit a park in the morning; always in the afternoon. But before they reach the park, they turn left again, onto the rue de Rome. Twice the woman stops on the sidewalk and looks behind her as though she senses that he is trailing her, so he follows at a distance, watching for the color of her clothes. To the left are the tracks leading from the Gare Saint-Lazare, fanning outward toward coastal destinations, Dieppe, Le Havre, Caen, Cherbourg. As the woman arrives near the Cours de Rome, she begins to walk faster, pulling the boy along, and Baptiste, breaking his cover, approaches her from behind. He is about to overtake her when a man calls out to her and she turns, looking through Baptiste. With the boy at her side, she rushes past him and into the Gare Saint-Lazare.

René says, "You're early."

"I was afraid. I didn't want to stay in the apartment any longer."

"Did you leave the letter?"

"Yes. On the kitchen table. Where's the car?"

"There isn't one. There's a change in the plan. We have to stay in the city."

"I don't understand."

"It doesn't matter. I have protection."

"What's that?"

"A gun."

She is certain her knees will fail her; soon she will be kneeling in terror. "Throw it away."

"It isn't loaded. It's for effect."

"You'll frighten the boy."

"He won't even see it. Now, let's get moving."

"Where are we going?"

"For a walk."

Baptiste is an ever-lengthening shadow. A man, a woman, a suitcase, and his son. He follows them east and then north until they arrive at the Impasse Saint-Michel, a poor cul-de-sac that the sun hasn't seen in a century. They enter one of the farthest buildings and descend the stairs, and Baptiste circles the block until he finds a passage into the back court and a dusty window, like the screen of an old cinema house, through which he can watch them. Within minutes, the man is gone, the woman and the boy left alone. Baptiste returns to the front of the building and waits a long moment to be certain that the man will not come back, and then he goes inside and down the stairs. There are two doors, both unmarked. He chooses the door on the right, turns the knob, and enters, but the room is empty. Going back to the hallway, he tries the door on the left, but it is locked. He holds his breath and knocks gently.

"René?" There is surprise in her voice.

"C'est moi."

"Déjà?"

At the exact moment at which she opens the door he pushes forward, entering swiftly and reaching a hand to her throat. "Not a word," he says. "Not one word."

There are pinups on the walls, yellow and unlovely. A postcard from Cannes, news clippings from the war, headlines of the liberation, an Iron Cross salvaged from a corpse, a calendar turned to March 1944. The only furniture is a broken desk and a mattress in one corner, and a single naked bulb burns from the ceiling, lighting the room a pale yellow.

The gun is on the table and Baptiste picks it up.

"It isn't loaded," Nadine tells him.

To answer her, he snaps open the cartridge and displays the bullets. Nadine holds a hand to her mouth and he realizes she didn't know.

He scatters the bullets like seeds throughout the room, then removes the barrel and throws it under the desk.

"He is your husband?"

"I am a widow."

He considers for a moment, noticing the scar, the pale C on her forehead. "I fought with the resistance. You were a collaborator?"

She answers that she collaborated.

"With an officer?"

"A simple private. A sentry."

"To whom you passed secrets."

"All I knew of myself. Of the war, nothing."

"And now he's dead."

"Yes," she says.

They hear footsteps in the street and she starts, thinking René has come back. But it is only a man and a woman leaving the building.

Baptiste says, "You could have screamed for help. They would have heard you."

"And done nothing. Prayed, perhaps."

"You haven't told me who the other man is."

"My cousin René. He's gone to get a car."

"When do you expect him?"

"In another hour. Maybe longer."

"When he comes back we won't be here."

The boys sits quietly on the mattress, a book in front of him. Nadine asks Baptiste if he has been following them before. "I know your face," she says.

Baptiste doesn't answer. "We have to take him home," he says.

"Will you call the police?"

He considers. If the police come, he will have to say who he is. No stranger would have followed them here.

"No," he tells her. "There's something else I want."

She says she has nothing to give him, no jewels and no money.

He gestures to the back window. "I was there. I saw you. After your cousin left, you took something from your purse and put it inside you. You were nearly in tears from the pain so I assume it was something valuable. A passport?"

She hesitates, wondering what else she might bargain with. A lifetime seems to swell inside of her and disappear. "I know a forger," she says. "In Pontoise. His name is Alain Marron."

"Is he expecting you?"

"No."

"How much will he want?"

She has no idea.

"How would I find him? Do you have his address?"

She says she hasn't seen him in years. "Search."

Footsteps cross the window above them and Baptiste begins to grow edgy. "There isn't time," he says. "Give me the passport and I'll let you go."

She answers that she needs it more than he does.

He says why doesn't she sleep with another diplomat.

Cursing, she lowers herself into a corner and leans against the wall. He watches as she lifts her skirt and reaches inward, grimacing with discomfort. When she cries aloud, the boy begins to cry as well and Baptiste reaches a hand to reassure him but the boy shrinks away.

We will never touch. He will never love me. I am a criminal.

After wiping the passport in the folds of her skirt, she hands it, still damp, to Baptiste.

"You still haven't told me who you are," she says.

"Who I was," he corrects her. "His father. I was his father."

In the French language, there is no distinction between the word *story* and the word *history*. Riding the train to Cherbourg, Baptiste ruminates on this, certain that a vital thread to the rest of his life lies within that fact. When he had seen Nadine remove the passport, wet and lightly laced with blood, from between her thighs, he had felt himself born again, at forty-seven, a Spanish national with three languages, so-so photographer, one-time dabbler in civil war and liberation, on his way to America, his story now his history.

The train stops in every God-forgotten village in overcast Normandy and from time to time he takes out the passport to gaze again at his new identity, saying *Grace, Grace, Grace,* to make it indelible, the name he will henceforth answer to. As the forger Alain has advised him, he touches and retouches every centimeter of paper, the cover, the seam of his photograph, to add smudges of his own fingerprints over those of Nadine, the forger, the diplomat. To make the document smell of him.

Feeling a knife at his throat, Alain Marron had lowered his price to a pack of Gauloises. "Treat me kindly and my hands won't shake," he had said. "Throw in a decent Bordeaux and we might even part friends."

There had been some difficulty with the paper; he had never worked with a similar surface and texture. He hadn't the right chemicals to dilute the ink and had seriously botched the birthdate, changing it from 1944 to 1914 instead of 1904, as Baptiste had asked. Baptiste had had to dye his hair and brows, claiming back fourteen years, a wrinkle in his act that he would just have to get used to. But Alain had been brilliant with the height and weight and had masterfully lifted the photo of the young boy from its seam and replaced it with the image of Baptiste, Grace incarnate, had altered the issuance and expiration dates, and as a bonus had forged two travel stamps, one for Spain and the other for Italy.

R from P and C from G. RACE, all in capitals. The addition of a preceding G completing the name and the first name, a half whitewash, becoming Santos from Hunter, the most difficult piece of business. Santos Grace. Say it to yourself when you awaken and before you sleep.

The train approaches Cherbourg, a boat, America. His blood grown thin with age and his name of new consequence, Baptiste lets slip the bonds of Europe.

But before his exodus he has performed an errand more painful than saying goodbye to a name he'd grown accustomed to. He has delivered his son to another man.

The boy had been reluctant to take his hand. Clutching his book to his chest, he had finally surrendered first a finger, then another, and at last a full palm to the dark hand that was offered to him.

The journey had been too brief: small recompense for a lifetime ransacked by stupid luck and untimely love. Down the Avenue de Clichy, past the fork to the Place de Clichy, crossing against insistent traffic to the other sidewalk. Just down the street was the rue Ballu, a left turn, and then the doorway. Once inside, Baptiste had instructed the boy to sit on the front steps and not to move.

"It is nearly dark. Your father will be home soon." The stairway had been lit with a yellow light, the carpet on the steps a worn green. Sadness clung to the whitewashed walls. "Do you understand me?"

A nodding. English Spoken Here.

Though he had known the boy would not understand him, he had said aloud that he had no wishes other than those that time could not grant him. "You will forget everything about this day. Now, sit here and do not move. Your father is coming for you. You won't have long to wait."

And had turned and with the first step had stopped dead still to wipe the pain from his face with angry fingers. His story now his history, he had felt something like a seasickness, a sudden loss of blood. And had walked out the door without daring to look back.

On a boy, sitting on the steps with a book of fables in his small hands.

EPILOG

SAIGON

So I'm back on the high wire without a net or an umbrella to break my fall, in a land with too much gravity, where the winds blow and everything left alive is out of luck and all the rest is bamboo or rubble, take your pick.

Understand this: I'm ignoring the fine lines and possible distinctions between a Randall truth and my own. I'm telling anyone who will listen that I'm looking for my son. If the ghost of Dune Buggy comes to visit me in the night for some split-hairs argument over genes and DNA, I'll just shrug and say it doesn't matter, even though somewhere in my secret heart it does and always will.

The French priest is dead and his mission has been burned. Rumor has it that the kids from his village have been trucked up north and I'm going to have to climb a long ladder of jungle to follow them. That jungle seems to reach into forever but somewhere it has to end. Wherever it does, I'll find the boy.

We're pulling out, I'm told. The war is on its last legs. The land has gone dry and dead and the war is lost, which partly explains the carny atmosphere, the selling of possessions, the lifetimes bartered for tickets on leaky boats to anywhere.

I'm sitting by the side of a muddy road, waiting for a truck to pass. One of ours. I light a match and watch the flame burn its way to my fingers. If it doesn't go out, I'll know I'm done for. I'm wearing khaki so those men in the trucks will see what language I speak. They won't know I'm obsessed until long after we've taken to the road. I will light more matches to test my luck. If the driver bothers me about it, I'll take his picture and then he'll be sorry he ever crossed my path.

We'll head north into the jungle. Beyond that jungle there is a green space, perhaps a mission. I know the terrain and can offer directions, tell them which way to go.

In the meantime I'll sit here wide-eyed, waiting on the flame.